DISTRIBUTION
OF THE ELEMENTS
IN OUR PLANET

Earth and Planetary Science Series

Patrick M. Hurley, *Consulting Editor*

AHRENS: DISTRIBUTION OF THE ELEMENTS IN OUR PLANET

DISTRIBUTION OF THE ELEMENTS IN OUR PLANET

L. H. AHRENS

PROFESSOR OF GEOCHEMISTRY
UNIVERSITY OF CAPETOWN

McGRAW-HILL BOOK COMPANY

NEW YORK   ST. LOUIS   SAN FRANCISCO
TORONTO   LONDON   SYDNEY

First McGraw-Hill Paperback Edition, 1965

Distribution of the Elements in Our Planet

Library of Congress Catalog Card Number 65-19852
  3 4 5 6 7 8 9 0 MU I 0
McGraw-Hill Paperbacks

FOREWORD

TO THE LAYMAN SCIENCE APPEARS MORE and more frequently in the guise of a mystery protected by a priesthood, and from which he is aware of a cloud-like explosion of new and ever more complex ideas. To the scientist, the quasi-religious face may be at most a regrettable mask of convenience, but the complexity is undeniable. The objective of this open ended series is to help in a small way both to remove the mask as well as any lingering need for it and to reduce somewhat the confusion and obscurity of important new advances—at least in the area of the earth and planetary sciences.

Each volume has the scope of a lecture series or a short college course. Each author is engaged in research on the subject in question. The books are brief so that the busy research worker will be able to bring his viewpoint, current ideas, and speculations to the reader with a minimum of time and effort. Thus he can present to the non-specialist reader an accurate account of those parts of the subject describable in every day language. To the specialist the author can give a separate development of physical and chemical formulations necessary for more technical parts of the subject matter.

The series as a whole will investigate the solid earth, and its fields, the oceans and atmosphere, and some aspects of space and planetary science. What precisely is the subject of each book depends on the background and the research of the author.

The author of this monograph, Dr. L. H. Ahrens, took his formal education in chemistry. However, most of his large research output has been in geochemistry. His subjects of particular interest have been spectrochemical investigations of trace element abundances, geochemical rules governing trace element abundances, geochronology, and isotope geochemistry. He has travelled, written, and lectured widely, and he has had formal affiliation with the faculties of M.I.T., Oxford University, and the University of Cape Town, where he is now Chairman of the Department of Geochemistry.

PATRICK HURLEY

PREFACE

BOTH FUNDAMENTAL AND APPLIED
science progress at an extraordinary pace.
Pace is controlled by many factors: some
are perhaps obvious and are geared to
urgent and immediate requirements of
our society; examples may be found in
medicine, military science, and divers
branches of technology. Other pace set-
ters derive their momentum from our
search for knowledge per se—scientific
enquiry for its own sake.

Endeavour in such "pure" science
covers an enormous range of disciplines,
and every now and again fresh names
enter our vocabulary to describe new
specializations. For example, in the early
nineteenth century, chemistry represented
a fairly well-defined subject, but by the

beginning of this century it was customary to distinguish three types of chemistry: inorganic, organic, and physical. Now a multitude of additional chemical disciplines have come into existence; analytical chemistry, structural chemistry, quantum chemistry, radiochemistry, nuclear chemistry, biochemistry, and geochemistry, among others.

The introduction of so many subdivisions may seem to represent a continuous breakdown, a schizophrenia, an ever increasing tendency toward specialization and pigeonholing. This is only true in part. We cannot in fact pigeonhole science; if we were to do so, it would become inert and sterile. Coupled with the tendency toward specialization is a strong reverse tendency—that of coalescence. It is in the coalescence and overlapping of disciplines that much of the momentum in the accelerated growth of science originates: examples are biophysics and biochemistry, geophysics and geochemistry.

In this book we are to deal with aspects of geochemistry. Though we may recognize a fairly distinct discipline in geochemistry, this new subject touches on a wide variety of fields: various branches of physics, chemistry, geology, mineralogy, petrology, and analytical chemistry with a little astronomy thrown in. Therein lies its vigor and its fascination.

As the term implies, geochemistry is a study of the chemistry of the earth, including the origin of our planet. The subject is vast and as yet only moderately well understood. Our particular interest here is with one major aspect of geochemistry, the manner in which the different elements have distributed themselves in our planet. The story is, I think, an interesting one.

L. H. AHRENS

CONTENTS

DISTRIBUTION
OF THE ELEMENTS
IN OUR PLANET

1 IN THE BEGINNING

Creation of the elements

The composition of our planet and the manner in which the elements have distributed themselves in it are closely linked to the entire history of the universe: To the first creation of elements and to the consequent formation of earth, planets, sun, and stars from some cosmic mixture of these elements. But how far back in time should we go?

The beginnings are shrouded in uncertainty, and the early history of the observable universe presents problems which may seem to be beyond the reach of imagination. For the specific purpose of studying element distributions in this planet, let us merely assume that at the dawn of time matter was dispersed throughout the universe in the form of its simplest elemental component, hydrogen. The atom of hydrogen is composed of a nuclear proton and an orbiting electron. If we make this assumption, astrophysicists and nuclear physicists are able to provide a plausible account of how atoms of dispersed hydrogen may condense. Under conditions of intense heat, they may undergo a series of nuclear reactions by means of which atoms of the heavier and more complex elements may be synthesized. The heat required to initiate the first nuclear reactions can evidently be supplied through gravitational potential energy which is released as the mass of hydrogen atoms condenses. This condensation hypothesis assumes conditions of distribution and movement which are highly speculative and need not detain us. Suffice it to say that once begun, the nuclear reactions themselves provide intense heat. Some may be cyclic and will act, therefore, as a sustaining source of energy. We are in fact briefly describing the evolution of a star. Nuclear reactions have been taking place in the hot interiors of stars, including our sun, ever since these bodies came into existence.

Though the life of a star is a long one, conditions within it change gradually; ultimately a stage of instability may be reached, due mainly to the fact that most of the nuclear fuel, hydrogen and helium, becomes exhausted. The star may explode as a supernova, during which process the conditions are such that various heavy elements, hitherto not produced in the star, may be synthesized. In fact, satisfactory conditions have evidently existed in stars for the creation of all elements through the appropriate nuclear reactions.

Stars eject part of their substance to outer space, either through an outright explosion, as in a supernova, or merely through continuous loss of material at their surfaces. Such stellar "ejecta" is commonly referred to as cosmic dust and is widely dispersed throughout interstellar space. It is from such cosmic substance that other components of our observable universe, younger stars and planets, including the members of our solar system, may eventually have evolved. But such a history strongly implies that the component stars and planets of the universe did not come into existence at the same time. A question therefore arises: how old is the solar system?

The age of the solar system

According to current astronomical thinking, the oldest stars which populate our galaxy are at least 10^{10} years (10,000 million years) old, and they may be even older. At the other extreme are stars so young that they are only now in the embryonic stages of development. Our solar system is probably "middle-aged" and is estimated to have come into existence approximately 6×10^9 (6,000 million) years ago. Although these figures are speculative, we come to firmer ground when we attempt to estimate the age of our planet. There is more certainty about when it was consolidated into its present form. Natural radioactivity, notably of the elements potassium, rubidium, thorium, and uranium, provides a means for estimating time.

Utilized first in 1908 by Boltwood in England, radioactive techniques have become highly developed and are widely applied for estimating the ages of hundreds of rocks and minerals from each of the principal continents. The same techniques have been applied to meteorites. Several important conclusions emerge from these measurements, one of which is particularly significant for our discussion; namely, that the oldest dated minerals from the major continents are about 3×10^9 (3,000 million) years old. Allowance of 1,000 million years or so for events which preceded the formation of the oldest rocks and minerals brings us to a magnitude of 4 to 5×10^9 years as the "age of the earth." This magnitude is close to the estimated ages of meteorites, and because the earth and meteorites are believed to have a common origin (Chapter 2), the evidence is strong that the earth originated some 4,000 to 5,000 million years ago.

Some early developments in the evolution of the solar system

We shall assume that some 6,000 million years ago the solar system formed from that cosmic dust which then existed in the region of space now occupied by the sun, ten planets, and their satellites. Eddies formed in the dust, and gravitational forces of attraction caused the cosmic dust cloud to accrete. The central and major proportion of the cloud condensed into what ultimately became a fiery sun. The remaining material, estimated at only 5 percent or so, became dispersed in the form of a rotating disc about the central mass. The disk then presumably broke up into eddies of irregular size which generally increased in volume with distance away from the central mass. These eddies of dust and gas eventually coalesced into distinct entities which are usually referred to as the protoplanets. Much of what happened at this time and thereafter is speculative and controversial; for our purpose we shall merely outline a tentative and simplified scheme of events.

Thus we shall further assume that at the time the protoplanets were formed, the protosun had not yet developed into a true sun; it was dark and cool. The protoearth was at this time enveloped by large quantities of gas (hydrogen, helium, neon, methane, and perhaps some water vapor), amounting to some 99 percent or so of the whole protoearth. Though the cosmic dust from which the protoearth accreted is thought to have been cool, once it condensed to a considerable degree, heating evidently took place. Without heat the protoplanet could not have evolved into its present condition. Such heat was evidently supplied in large part by radioactivity which would have been far more intense some 5,000 million years ago, compared with the situation today. The reason for this is easy to understand.

The radioactive process is one of nuclear breakdown in which the ejected particles generate heat by impact on surrounding matter. With the passage of time, however, more and more of the radioactive nuclei break down and activity becomes progressively less; as a consequence, heat generated by radioactivity diminishes. The rate of radioactive disintegration is exponential. If we move back in time and consider nuclei whose half-lives (the time taken for a given number of nuclei to reduce to half the original number) are fairly small compared with the magnitude of the age of the earth, but which nevertheless still exist, we reach a stage when activity would be very high and heating very intense. The isotopes K^{40} (half-life $= 1.31 \times 10^9$ years) and U^{235} (half-life $= 7.1 \times 10^8$ years) are perhaps particularly significant in this respect; if cosmic dust were to have condensed say some 10,000 million years ago, radioactive heating would have been so great that the whole mass would have melted and vaporized completely. At a relatively younger age (say 5,000 million years ago), heat from these radioactive sources would still be intense, but not necessarily sufficient to melt the whole of the condensing embryonic planet. Be that as it may, it is necessary only to assume that radioactive and other sources of heat caused some of the protoplanet to melt. Some chemical reactions would then have begun. Because the melting point of a substance increases with pressure which in turn increases with depth, melting in the embryonic planet would presumably have begun near the surface.

As radioactivity diminished with the passage of time and the temperature of the partly molten earth began to drop, a series of significant events took place. They culminated in consolidation of the solid earth more or less in its present form.

The emphasis in this book is on the distribution of elements in the solid earth. But the atmosphere and oceans are also significant planetary features and will first detain us briefly. Before we return to solid earth, moreover, we shall consider in some detail the composition of that cosmic substance from which the solar system originated. If earth and the other components of the solar system were created out of dust, as we assume, their evolutionary fate was determined in large measure by the abundances of elements in that dust.

The atmosphere and oceans

The protosun may have been dark and cool (page 4) at first, but once its temperature rose as a true fiery sun evolved, the intense heat drove off a major proportion of the primitive protoearth atmosphere. Only a small proportion of the early atmosphere has remained and the present atmosphere should not be regarded as a remnant of the primitive atmosphere associated with the protoearth.

Components of the present atmosphere together with the water of the oceans have apparently been generated by "degassing" volatile components, including water vapor, from the earth's interior. The mechanism is that of volcanic activity, which has persisted in varying degrees throughout geological time, starting with the consolidation of the solid earth. Volcanic activity is, however, not the only source from which components of the atmosphere have been produced. For example, much of the atmospheric oxygen has been produced through photosynthesis, and a major proportion of atmospheric argon, the third most abundant gas in the atmosphere, owes its origin to the radioactivity of potassium.

Two kinds of events explain most of the salts and minerals dissolved in the oceans. Volcanic activity is again partially responsible. But a major proportion of several constituents of sea water, including the sodium in sodium chloride, the principal salt, has originated from the slow decomposition (weathering) of rocks. Some of their constituents are eventually carried in solution into rivers which transport them to the sea.

2 THE ABUNDANCES OF THE ELEMENTS

WE HAVE NOTED THAT IT WAS THE composition of primitive solar dust which ultimately led to the present state of affairs on our planet. It should be borne in mind that in spite of some close similarities, even some equivalencies between the composition of the earth today and that of the primitive cosmic dust, in other respects they differ markedly. The differences are mainly due to the loss of various volatile material during the early periods of our planet's evolution.

Three kinds of evidence provide information about the composition of the primitive solar dust: evidence from meteorites and evidence from the sun and other stars provide concrete information. The third type is evidence which stems principally from theoretical considerations of interest to the nuclear and astrophysicist. They are complex and beyond the scope of this book, but we should bear in mind that, provided certain assumptions are made, it is possible for the physicist to estimate the abundances of several of the elements.

Meteorites as a source of abundance data

In addition to details about the composition of the primitive cosmic dust prevailing in our region of the universe some 5,000 million years ago, meteoritic data provide an invaluable guide to the abundance of elements both in the earth as a whole (average composition) and in its principal components (page 20). Both astronomical and chemical evidence lead to the conclusion that the earth and the meteorites had a common origin.

If this were not so and if meteorites had originated elsewhere in our observable universe, their chemical composition might have differed quite markedly from that of our planet. Abundance data based on the analyses of meteorites could then be quite misleading, for the components of our observable universe do not have the same composition. They contain the same elements, but the proportions may vary. Analyses of spectra radiated by stars provide unequivocal evidence that although the composition of many stars is similar, there are several notable differences. Some stars evidently contain relatively high concentrations of certain elements, barium and the rare earth elements for example, which by comparison are rare in our sun (and also in the earth).

What then is the evidence that earth and meteorites have a common origin? Aside from the fact that their respective ages are similar, there is the interesting fact that the isotopic composition of some elements in both the earth and the meteorites is identical. Furthermore, recent measurements have shown that the abundance ratio of the alkali metals potassium and rubidium appears to be the same, or very similar, in earth and meteorites. Such equivalence in isotopic composition and element ratio could only arise if the elements composing the earth and the meteorites were created under identical conditions; in other words, they may be presumed to have had a common origin. To be sure, the isotopic composition of some elements may differ in the earth and the meteorites, but these differences can usually be ascribed to the influence of radio-activity or the action of cosmic rays.

Though we may safely assume that the constituent elements of both our earth and the meteorites had a common origin, a note of caution must be sounded when these extra-terrestrial objects are used to provide abundance data on the stuff from which the earth and solar system originated. In the first place, meteorites have had a rough passage through space. Intense heating through contact with the earth's atmosphere may have caused a loss of their gaseous components and also of some very volatile metals. Secondly, there is the problem of weighting. Several varieties of meteorites exist. Some are rare and some are common, and we must mix them in their correct proportion in order to obtain a reasonably accurate idea of the abundances of the elements in the material out of which the planet evolved.

Meteorites vary in several respects, but they can be classified according to certain characteristic properties. Three principal types are usually distinguished: *irons*, *stony irons*, and *stones*. As the term implies, irons are in fact composed mainly of metallic iron. Several other elements are also concentrated in the irons: gold, the platinum group of metals, and nickel are examples. The composition of the stony irons falls roughly midway between that of the irons and the stones. The stones may themselves be divided into two subtypes; *chondrites* and *anchondrites.* The former subtype is by far the more abundant.

But how can we estimate the relative abundances (proportions) of the different types of meteorites so that we can mix them in correct proportions? The reader who has visited museums in which meteorites are displayed will probably come to the conclusion that the irons are far more abundant than the stones. Such a conclusion may be false, for this reason: a high proportion of all meteorites which ultimately find a home in a museum have been sent there by someone who happened to chance upon a strange looking object during a walk across open fields. Irons do have an unusual appearance and are likely to be noticed, whereas the stones are not conspicuous, particularly if they have been exposed to the actions of wind and rain for some time, and are more easily passed by.

Rather than rely on chance discoveries of meteorites (the "finds") as an indication of the proportions of different types of meteorites, it is safer to base our judgment on the "falls"; these represent meteorites which have been picked up soon after they were actually seen to fall. Some 1,500 to 1,600 meteorites have been reported and described. Their distribution, according to "falls," "finds," and type, is given in Table 2–1.

TABLE 2–1

	"Falls"		"Finds"		Total	
	no.	%	no.	%	no.	%
Irons	42	6	503	59	545	35
Stony irons	12	2	55	6	67	4
Stones	628	92	304	35	932	61
Total	682	100	862	100	1544	100

If we use the "falls" rather than the "finds" as our guide, it is quite clear that stones greatly outnumber irons and stony irons. Because the stones are composed principally of chondrites, let us give particular attention to these meteorites.

The principal component (some 80 to 90 percent) of the chondrites is the so-called silicate phase, made up mainly of the silicates of magnesium and iron. There are two other fairly abundant phases: a metal phase, mainly iron, and a sulphide phase composed mainly of iron sulphide and commonly referred to as troilite. Though the composition of chondritic meteorites is fairly uniform, several distinct types have been distinguished. One rare but particularly interesting group is commonly referred to as the carbonaceous chondrites. As their name implies, these meteorites contain organic matter and are sometimes regarded as representative of the solid nonvolatile substance of primitive solar dust. For our purposes we shall use the grand average for all chondrites.

Evidence from the sun and stars

In addition to the abundance data provided by the meteorites, supplementary information may be obtained via the stars and, in particular, the sun. The possibility that such information might well be used to estimate quantitatively the abundance relationships of elements has presented an exciting problem to theoretical physicists. The solution has in principle depended upon spectrum analysis, roughly as follows: at high temperatures, such as those prevailing in the sun, atoms of different elements radiate characteristic spectral lines. The "composition" (number of lines and their wavelengths) of the sun's spectrum is determined mainly by the elements which happen to be present. The *brightness* of these lines (their relative intensities) depends, however, on several factors, including the relative abundances of the elements; for any given conditions of temperature and pressure, spectral lines are brighter, the greater the abundance of the element. It is possible, therefore, to obtain a reasonably good quantitative estimate of relative abundances of the elements in the solar system by examining the intensities of lines in the sun's spectrum. For most of the so-called metallic elements, the data supplied by meteorites are more satisfactory than those supplied by the sun, but the sun has a special place for some of the elements which are volatile. For example, a volatile element may escape from meteorites when they are intensely heated as they pass through earth's atmosphere. This being the case, analysis of the lines of volatile element in the sun's spectrum would provide a more reliable estimate of its abundance in the solar system than would analysis of a meteorite.

Composition of primitive solar dust

Though it is difficult to estimate precisely the abundances of the elements in primitive solar dust, the data from meteorites and solar and stellar spectra, together with theoretical considerations, provide us with a reasonable approximation of the correct composition. The abundance relationships are shown in Fig. 2-1, where abundance is related to the atomic number of each element.

Several distinct features stand out in the abundance diagram. The range in abundance is enormous, a feature which may not strike the reader unless he has noticed that the vertical scale is logarithmic and not linear. The lightest elements, hydrogen and helium, are by far the most abundant; this feature is characteristic throughout most of the observable universe. In fact the intensities of the spectral lines emitted by different stars indicate that hydrogen and helium are

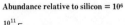

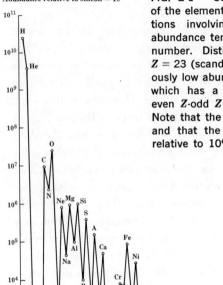

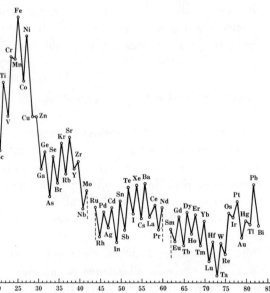

FIG. 2-1 "Cosmic" abundance diagram of the elements. Aside from sharp fluctuations involving the lightest elements, abundance tends to decrease with atomic number. Distinct exceptions appear at $Z = 23$ (scandium), which has a conspicuously low abundance and at $Z = 26$ (iron) which has a very high abundance. The even Z-odd Z effect is clearly developed. Note that the vertical scale is logarithmic and that the estimated abundances are relative to 10^6 atoms of silicon.

usually so abundant that most other elements may be regarded as "traces" only. The heavier elements, furthermore, tend to be less abundant than the lighter ones. Major exceptions to this trend are the light elements, lithium, beryllium and boron (conspicuously low), scandium (also low), and iron. The latter, a moderately heavy element, is much more abundant than it should be according to the abundance-atomic number trend.

One striking feature of the diagram is the jaggedness of the graph line. This "seesaw" effect occurs because, almost without exception, elements with even atomic numbers are more abundant than their odd-numbered neighbors. The "seesaw" effect was observed in 1916 simultaneously by Oddo in Germany and Harkins in the United States and may be referred to, therefore, as the Oddo-Harkins rule. It will be of interest to observe later (Chapter 8) that the "even-odd" pattern for one group of elements, the rare earths ($Z = 57$ to $Z = 71$), in this "cosmic" abundance diagram is reasonably well-preserved in our planet.

Explanations of these abundance features currently intrigues physicists and astrophysicists, and certain of their findings bear directly upon the distribution of elements in the earth.

Elements have been and are being created in the hot interiors of stars by a variety of nuclear reactions (hydrogen burning, helium burning, thermonuclear reactions, neutron capture reactions, and others). Prevailing conditions such as temperature and pressure and certain properties of the nuclei of the isotopes of atoms (structure and the ability to capture neutrons), may also strongly influence abundance. An example will illustrate one effect of a nuclear property on abundance.

Compare the isotopic abundance distribution of two elements, tin and cerium. Although the nuclei of all the stable (nonradioactive) isotopes of tin and most of those of cerium may be regarded as "normal," one cerium isotope (Ce^{140}) is quite unusual. Its nucleus contains 82 neutrons (N), and it has been recognized for some time that the presence of such a large number of neutrons in the nucleus endows it with rather special properties. The effect of "magic" $N = 82$ on isotopic abundance is clearly seen in Fig. 2-2 where the abundance of Ce^{140} is conspicuously elevated.

FIG. 2–2   The effect of the "magic" neutron number $N = 82$ on the relative abundances of isotopes. Note the elevation of Ce^{140}. The abundance distribution of the tin isotopes may be regarded as fairly typical for many even Z elements.

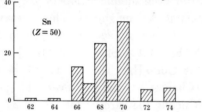

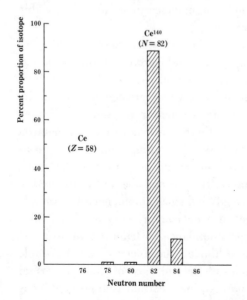

Average composition of the solid earth

This chapter has so far dealt principally with the composition of the primitive cosmic substance from which our planet and solar system evolved. Gaseous constituents, notably hydrogen and helium, were particularly abundant. In the next chapter we will examine the abundances of the elements and their distribution in the solid earth as it now exists. Because during its evolution our planet lost a high proportion of its gaseous and volatile components, the abundance relationships of Fig. 2-2 do not represent present conditions. The average composition of the solid earth today is best revealed in the average composition of chondrites, the commonest meteorites. Data on the most abundant constituent elements of chondrites are given in Table 2-2. Complete data on all elements are given in the Appendix.

TABLE 2–2

Element	Percent
SiO_2	38.04
MgO	23.84
FeO	12.45
Al_2O_3	2.50
CaO	1.95
Na_2O	0.98
K_2O	0.17
Cr_2O_3	0.36
MnO	0.25
TiO_2	0.11
P_2O_5	0.21
Fe	11.76
Ni	1.34
Co	0.08
FeS	5.73
Total Fe	25.07

With respect to the metallic elements, three—iron, silicon, and magnesium—are by far the most abundant. Aluminum and calcium come next, followed by sodium. Iron is present in three forms: metallic iron (Fe), iron combined with oxygen, and iron combined with sulfur; the geochemical significance of these characteristics is discussed in Chapter 4.

3 THE COMPOSITION OF THE PRINCIPAL STRUCTURAL COMPONENTS OF THE EARTH

THIS PLANET IS NOT A HOLLOW SPHERE, nor are the elements of which it is composed concentrated at its surface. The surface and near-surface regions can obviously be observed directly and in detail; on the other hand, information about the earth's interior is indirect and deductive. Nevertheless, we have quite a good notion as to the nature of the earth's interior. Expensive and complex projects such as that of the "Mohole" are designed to improve that knowledge, but striking as these efforts may be, they cannot take us far into the deep interior. We must be reconciled to the fact that it will not be possible to obtain samples from great depths.

Earth structure according to geophysical evidence

A first question is whether the composition of the earth is more or less uniform throughout. If this were so, the elements would be fairly evenly distributed right down to the deep interior in proportions similar to those found in the chondritic meteorites (Table 2-2). But this is emphatically not the case. Our certainty about distribution in the deep interior stems not from samples taken from there, but from certain physical, or more correctly, geophysical evidence.

Geophysicists have for some time been able to follow the passage through the earth of so-called seismic waves generated either by earthquakes or by man-made explosions that have been designed specifically for the purpose. Seismic waves travel with speeds which depend on the medium through which they pass; the denser the material, the greater their velocity. Thus, velocity is relatively low (1.5 km/sec) in sea water which has a density of a little more than 1, and about 4 times faster (5.1 to 6.2 km/sec) in common rock basalt with a density of about 2.9.

Extensive studies on seismic waves show that their velocity is at a minimum at the earth's surface and tends to increase toward the interior. Evidently the interior is more dense. But as the depth increases, sharp changes of velocity (discontinuities) may be encountered. For example, at a depth of 30 to 40 km below the continents and about 10 km below the surface of the major oceans, velocity varies from a value of 7 km/sec to one of 8 km/sec. Discontinuities of this kind are evidently due to a change in the physical nature of the material, and may also involve a change in chemical composition.

Figure 3-1 provides an indication of the structure of the earth based mainly on geophysical evidence. Three principal components are distinguished: *core*, *mantle*, and *crust*. Secondary discontinuities lead to a further subdivision of the mantle and core, as indicated in the diagram. Granted that these principal divisions and subdivisions can be made, it is up to the geochemist to provide some notion about the composition of each principal structural component.

Composition of the core

To ascertain the probable composition of the earth's core, it is helpful to return to the semi-speculative chronological approach adopted in Chapter 1. We shall go back to a stage in the evolution of the planet when it was cooling and consolidating into its present condition from a partly molten state. At that time events occurred which were to lead to the so-called *primary partitioning* of the elements.

The actual course of events would depend in the first place on the relative abundances (composition) of the elements in

FIG. 3–1   The principal structural components of the earth based mainly on data from seismic wave velocities. Note that the crust of our planet represents a thin "skin." The mantle is the major component.

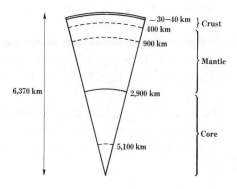

the cooling earth. Those elements which were more abundant tended to play a major role, particularly if they were chemically active. The nonmetal oxygen would have been of outstanding importance because it is both abundant and highly active. The nonmetal sulfur would also have been important, but distinctly less so than oxygen.

Oxygen and sulfur would tend to combine with highly active metals. Less frequently they combined with the less chemically active elements such as iron, although it would have been present in abundance. Abundant silicon would participate in the reactions involving oxygen, leading ultimately to the production of silicates, but it would not combine with sulfur. Sulfur would combine with those metals with a distinct affinity for it. Once all the oxygen and sulfur had been consumed in reactions with the active metals, excess iron would separate in the form of droplets. Because of their comparatively high density, these drops of iron would sink through the molten or viscous silicates toward the center of the planet, eventually concentrating there into a central metallic mass, the core of the earth.

Several of the rarer metals which are not chemically very active, gold, platinum, and nickel for example, would react to only a moderate extent with oxygen and sulfur. The excess free rare metals would tend to concentrate in the descending iron droplets and would also ultimately find a home in the core.

The core itself is not completely homogeneous, as indicated in Fig. 3-1. It is possible that the inner core is solid and is surrounded by a liquid phase. These are problems which can never be completely resolved; speculation is, in fact, rife on the actual nature of the core. We need not, however, become involved in the controversy. There is strong evidence that the earth's core is metallic, whether or not part of it is in the liquid state.

Composition of the mantle

In the mantle which surrounds the core it is commonly assumed that dense silicates, mainly those of magnesium and iron, predominate. Pressures in the earth's interior are very high and if a certain threshold pressure on a substance such as magnesium silicate is exceeded, the constituent atoms may rearrange themselves into a more closely packed structure. Some of the secondary discontinuities in the mantle may be due to such physical changes—referred to usually as polymorphic changes—in which chemical composition remains, nevertheless, unchanged.

Although the problem of the composition of the mantle as a whole, and the upper mantle in particular, is one which is currently receiving worldwide attention, it is as yet only partly resolved. Much of the mantle material can be described as "dense silicates of iron and magnesium," but significant quantities of the abundant elements aluminum, sodium, potassium, and calcium must be present also. Part of the problem, therefore, is to determine the relative proportions of each of these as well as other elements both in the lower and the upper mantle.

One particularly interesting pointer to the composition of the upper mantle comes from the so-called cognate xenoliths. These are fragments of rock which have been brought to the earth's surface as a result of their entrapment in magmas that originated at depth whence, by one mechanism or another, they have risen. Xenoliths have been found in basalts and in the so-called *kimberlite* pipes which are particularly abundant in South Africa. Some of them are diamond bearing. The very presence of diamonds in the kimberlite pipes indicates that the kimberlitic material must have formed at considerable depths where the conditions—notably the pressure and temperature—were such that the gems would develop. Most of the xenolithic fragments belong to two main rock types, peridotite (composed mainly of Mg-Fe silicates), and the garnet-bearing rock, eclogite. The composition of average peridotite is provided by the data in column two of Table 3-1 (page 28).

Complex indeed is the history of the events involved in the process of cooling which eventually lead to the separation of the silicates of the mantle from those of the crust. One brief and perhaps oversimplified version holds that as the silicate mass cooled, those silicates with the highest melting points will crystallize first. These are the Mg-Fe silicates, commonly referred to as the ferromagnesian minerals. Because of their high densities, the ferromagnesian minerals might tend to concentrate toward the bottom of the cooling silicate mass, consolidating there ultimately to form the main part of the mantle. (Be it said at once that this scheme of events does not have general support. I use it, nevertheless, because it can be supported and some of the ideas that evolve from it contribute to discussions that follow. Alternative descriptions can claim no greater unanimity.) The remaining relatively light liquid would eventually solidify and form the substance of the earth's crust. Events of a similar nature were evidently involved in the production of the principal igneous rocks within the crust (page 26).

The crust of the earth

The crust of the earth of course surrounds the mantle. Less speculation is required because more factual information is at hand; nevertheless, there are several uncertainties. When we began our study of the composition of the earth as a whole we looked first to geophysical evidence to tell us whether the

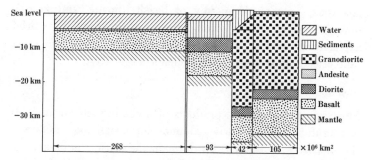

FIG. 3–2 Schematic section of the crust of the earth. Whereas in the continental regions granitic rocks are present in great abundance overlying the basaltic rocks, these rocks are apparently absent from the oceanic areas. (From "Crust of the Earth," Fig. 1, p. 128 of *Geol. Soc. America*, Special Paper 62, 1955. A. Poldervaart, ed.)

earth possessed a distinct structure or not. Our approach to the problem of the composition of the crust will be the same. Now we enquire, therefore, whether geophysical evidence has provided information about the structure of the crust. There is the possibility naturally that the crust is more or less uniform in composition and without distinct structure. Geophysical evidence is quite clear on this point, however. Together with geological evidence, it indicates the presence of distinct structure in the crust.

Some of the more notable features are shown in Fig. 3-2, a schematic section through both the continental and the oceanic regions of the crust. The difference in crustal thickness (10 km in oceanic areas and about 30 to 40 km in continental areas) is clear. Several of the main structural features may be described in terms of the disposition of the principal crustal components: the water of the great oceans; the sediment which covers rocks of igneous origin, both in the oceans and on the continents; and finally, the most abundant component, "igneous rock," composed mainly of basalt, diorite, and granite plus granodiorite. The term "igneous rock" requires a brief explanation before we discuss the composition of the crust (the crustal abundances of the elements).

IGNEOUS ROCKS

Most igneous rocks are products of a cooling silicate melt. If temperature drops slowly, a condition which may obtain if the melt freezes fairly deep down in the crust, the crystalline igneous rock produced is usually classed as *plutonic*; because of slow crystallization, its texture is likely to be coarse. Granite, granodiorite, diorite, and gabbro are examples of common plutonic rocks. When a molten silicate melt (magma) rises to the surface of the crust, emerges as a flow, and freezes, cooling may be rapid. The rock that results is classed as *volcanic* or *effusive*. Because of rapid crystallization of the lava, the texture of a volcanic rock is usually fine-grained. Rhyolite, dacite, andesite, and basalt are examples. The composition of each of these four volcanic rocks matches that of each of the four plutonic rocks in the order in which they appear: rhyolite is the volcanic equivalent of granite, basalt is the volcanic equivalent of gabbro, and so on. The breakdown of plutonic and volcanic rocks into four categories is based mainly on chemical composition.

The crustal igneous rocks apparently were not all created when the earth consolidated into its principal components. There is little doubt that large volumes of granite and basalt were formed early in the history of the earth. On the other hand, evidence from the ages of igneous rocks, obtained both by radioactivity measurements and by geological observations, demonstrates that both plutonic and effusive igneous rocks have formed from time to time throughout a major part of the earth's lifetime over a period of at least 3,000 million years. In a sense therefore we must regard the crust, or at least parts of it, as being in a continuous state of evolution.

In part, continuous evolution of the crust occurs as a consequence of the action of various weathering agents such as rain and temperature change. Many of the early crustal rocks decomposed. The resultant detrital material—sediment—would find a home in the deep oceans, accumulating there in great thickness. A stage might ultimately be reached when the stress of the overlying sediments would become so great that underlying crustal or upper-mantle rock would begin to melt. This remelted silicate could freeze at depth, after reduction of pressure, or might get squeezed into crustal cracks and fractures and perhaps even appear on the crustal surface. In this fashion, a fresh generation of igneous rocks, plutonic and volcanic, may be produced. Events such as these are part of the general process of mountain building from sedimentary material.

The evolutionary processes in the crust are complex, but need not concern us further. For our immediate purpose of estimating the composition of the crust we should recall that igneous rock, whether formed early or late in the evolution of the crust, is the principal crustal component and that granite plus granodiorite and basalt are by far the most abundant varieties of igneous rock.

COMPOSITION OF THE CRUST

The estimated composition of the crust together with some of the common varieties of rock are given in Table 3-1. Data on peridotite and shale, the commonest sedimentary rock, are included for comparison. The values given under "crust" are based on a 1 to 1 weighting of the commonest igneous rocks, basalt and granite. Table 3-1 refers only to the abundant elements, but the reader may refer to the Appendix for the estimated abundances of nearly all the elements, abundant and rare, in the crust.

Each variety of igneous rock is composed of one or more constituent minerals. Table 3-2 gives the proportion of these minerals in the crust, arranged in order of decreasing abun-

TABLE 3–1

Con-stituent	Peridotite (ultra-basic rock), %	Basaltic rock (basic rock), %	Inter-mediate rock, %	Granitic rock, %	Crust, %	Shale, %
SiO_2	43.5	48.5	54.5	69.1	58.7	58.1
TiO_2	0.8	1.8	1.5	0.5	1.2	0.7
Al_2O_3	2.	15.5	16.4	14.5	15.	15.4
Fe_2O_3	2.5	2.8	3.3	1.7	2.3	4.
FeO	9.9	8.1	5.2	2.2	5.2	2.5
MnO	0.2	0.17	0.15	0.07	0.12	
MgO	37.	8.6	3.8	1.1	4.9	2.4
CaO	3.	10.7	6.5	2.6	6.7	3.1
Na_2O	0.4	2.3	4.2	3.9	3.1	1.3
K_2O	0.1	0.7	3.2	3.8	2.3	3.2

dance. The estimated values should be regarded as approximate, though good enough to indicate reasonably accurately the proportions of the different minerals found in the average crustal igneous rocks.

In the discussion on element distribution in the crust (Chapters 5, 6, 7, and 8), emphasis will be placed on the most abundant crustal components, the igneous rocks. There are, of course, many other geological substances aside from the oceans and atmosphere. These include sedimentary rocks, metamorphic rocks, pegmatites, and ore deposits.

Sedimentary rocks originate through the compaction and consolidation of the various products of the decomposition of igneous and other rocks. Shale is the most abundant sedimentary rock, followed by limestone and sandstone. Metamorphic rocks are "re-worked" rocks, so to speak. Through the action of intense heat and pressure, resulting from volcanic activity and movements within the earth's crust, preexisting rocks whether igneous or sedimentary, can be transformed into new varieties, the metamorphic rocks. Pegmatites are vein-like bodies which are usually associated with igneous rocks. They may be taken to represent the residua of the fractional crystallization of the silicate melts from which the main mass of igneous rocks originate (page 26). Pegmatites frequently contain high enrichments of rare elements. The term "ore" merely means an economically exploitable geological substance; the term tends, however, to be restricted to minerals of the metals. Detailed descriptions of sedimentary rock, metamorphic rock, pegmatite, and ore may be sought in geology texts.

TABLE 3–2

Mineral	Percent proportion	
Alkali feldspar (1 part orthoclase, $KAlSi_3O_8$, and 1 part Albite, $NaAlSi_3O_8$)	31.	Total feldspar (60.2)
Plagioclase feldspar ($NaAlSi_3O_8 \rightarrow CaAl_2Si_2O_8$)	29.2	
Quartz (SiO_2)	12.4	
Pyroxene [$Ca(Mg,Fe)Si_2O_6$]	12.	
Oxides of iron and titanium (magnetite, Fe_3O_4; hematite, Fe_2O_3; ilmenite, $Fe^{II}Ti^{IV}O_3$)	4.1	
Biotite mica (complex K,Mg,Fe,Al,Ti, hydroxy-fluo silicate)	3.8	
Olivine [$(Fe,Mg)_2SiO_4$]	2.6	
Muscovite (complex K,Al hydroxy-fluo silicate)	1.4	
Other minerals	3.5	
Total	100.	

4 A GEOCHEMICAL CLASSIFICATION OF THE ELEMENTS

IN THE EARTH'S IRON CORE CERTAIN elements—gold, platinum, and nickel are examples—may be highly concentrated (page 22). Others again appear to concentrate in silicate rocks of the crust, whereas yet others may tend to combine with sulfur and concentrate in sulfur minerals. It has been noted also (page 12) that many meteorites are characterized by the presence of three principal solid phases, iron, sulfide (troilite), and silicate, in each of which different elements tend to concentrate. A similar distribution pattern emerges when ores are treated in blast furnaces for the purpose of producing metals. A flux is added to the ore and the mixture is heated to a high temperature at which the ore is decomposed by chemical reactions. The whole mass becomes molten and on cooling, three phases appear: a silicate *slag* enriched in the elements bonded to oxygen, a sulfide *matte* composed mainly of elements with distinct affinity for sulfur, and the metal itself which is rarely in a high state of purity.

On the basis of these tendencies, V. M. Goldschmidt suggested in 1922 a geochemical classification of the elements. The proposed terms and the corresponding tendencies are as follows:

Term	*Tendency*
siderophile (iron phase)	tendency to be associated with metallic iron
chalcophile (sulfide phase-troilite)	tendency to be bound to sulfur (affinity for sulfur)
lithophile (silicate phase)	tendency to be bound to oxygen (affinity for oxygen)
atmophile	tendency to occur as a gaseous component of the atmosphere

Other tendencies may exist, but here we shall concern ourselves mainly with the first three groups listed above, *siderophile*, *chalcophile*, and *lithophile*. A grouping of elements according to such tendencies—also called a geochemical classification of elements—is shown in Table 4-1.

Such tendencies vary considerably in degree. Thus, gold and the platinum group of elements show a strong siderophile tendency, much stronger than say, tin and germanium. The lithophile (silicate phase) tendency of the alkali metals (lithium, sodium, potassium, rubidium, and cesium) is so strong that the detection of these elements in the sulfide and metal phases is impossible without special effort. Conversely, some elements such as iron appear under more than one heading showing therefore more than one tendency. Where the tendency of the element is weaker, its symbol appears in a bracket.

TABLE 4–1

Siderophile			Chalcophile			Lithophile				
Fe	Co	Ni	Cu	Ag		Li	Na	K	Rb	Cs
Ru	Rh	Pd	Zn	Cd	Hg	Be	Mg	Ca	Sr	Ba
Os	Ir	Pt	Ga	In	Tl	B	Al	Sc	Y	
Au	Re	Mo	(Ge)	(Sn)	Pb					
Ge	Sn		As	Sb	Bi		Rare earths			
C	P		S	Se	Te	(C)	Si	Ti	Zr	Hf
(Pb)	(As)	(W)	(Fe)		(Mo)					Th
					(Cr)	(P)	V	Nb	Ta	
						O	Cr	W	U	
						(H)	F	Cl	Br	I
						(Tl)	(Ga)		(Ge)	
						(Fe)	Mn			

Theoretical basis for the Goldschmidt classification

The Goldschmidt classification is essentially empirical, but it can be put on a reasonably sound theoretical footing. Many distinctly lithophile elements are those which have their valence electrons outside closed shells of 8 electrons, whereas many of the chalcophile elements have their valence electrons outside closed shells of 18 electrons. With few exceptions, siderophile elements are typically those which belong to the so-called "transition-group" in the Periodic Table. (The complete Periodic Table may be found in the Appendix.)

Though these relationships are of interest, they do not in themselves give us much insight to the actual causes of the three geochemical tendencies. Two general features may be borne in mind when seeking an explanation: first, siderophile elements are not chemically combined when present in the metallic state, and second, although the chalcophile and lithophile elements are in chemical combination—with sulfur and oxygen, respectively—the chemical bonding in the sulfide minerals is largely covalent, whereas bonding in the silicate minerals may at first approximation be regarded as ionic.

SIDEROPHILE TENDENCY

Let us begin with the siderophile problem: why do some elements tend to occur in the native state (not chemically bound) and associated with metallic iron? The siderophile elements evidently do not easily enter into chemical combination with other elements because their valence electrons are not readily available. At the other extreme are some elements, the alkali metals for example, which are highly active, so chemically active in fact that it is difficult to keep them in an uncombined state; they tend to react with most substances which they contact. Such elements tend to be chalcophile or lithophile, but not siderophile.

The reactivity of an element depends partly on the electronic structure of its atoms (the number and arrangement of its electrons) and partly on the firmness with which its outermost valence electrons are bound in the atom. Such firmness of binding itself depends on electronic structure, in particular the efficiency with which a given arrangement of electrons screens (shields) the positive charge on the nucleus. If screening by the inner electrons is efficient, the outermost valence electrons may be very loosely held and readily available for chemical combination, and vice versa. The *ionization potential*, defined as "the energy required to remove completely an electron from an atom" provides a good quantitative measure of the tightness with which an electron is held in an atom. The ionization potential may be expressed in terms of electron volts (eV). If much energy is required to remove an electron, it is evidently firmly bound and the converse is also true.

Sodium and copper may be used to exemplify this reasoning.

Both elements belong to the first group in the Periodic Table. Accordingly, the atoms of sodium and copper contain a single electron outside a so-called closed shell of electrons, 8 in sodium and 18 in copper. The first ionization potential of sodium is 5.1 volts as compared with a distinctly higher value of 7.7 volts for copper. This information may be understood to mean that the single outer (valence) electron in the copper atom is more firmly held than in the sodium atom, presumably because the screening by the 18-electron shell in copper is less efficient than that of the 8-electron shell in sodium. Copper is chemically far less active than sodium.

First ionization potentials of the Group I elements are listed in Table 4-2.

The relatively large difference between the ionization potentials of the two groups of elements is striking. Note also the anomalous behavior of gold: The trend in the alkali metal group indicates that there is usually a fall in ionization potential when passing from lighter to heavier elements in a group. Yet the ionization potential of gold is greater than that of copper and silver. The valence electron in gold is so firmly held that this element is indeed loath to react with atoms of other elements; in nature it exhibits an extreme siderophile tendency. Copper and silver show fairly distinct siderophile tendencies, but far less than gold. The alkali metals show none.

TABLE 4–2

Element, 8 electron	I_1, volts	Element, 18 electron	I_1, volts
Li	5.3		
Na	5.1		
K	4.3	Cu	7.7
Rb	4.1	Ag	7.5
Cs	3.9	Au	9.2

As a measure of the firmness with which electrons are bound to atoms, ionization potentials may be applied reasonably well also to some other groups of elements. In the transition metals of Group VIII in the Periodic Table, the platinum group are by far the most siderophile, followed by nickel, cobalt, and iron, in that order. Their respective ionization potentials fall in the same order.

LITHOPHILE-CHALCOPHILE RELATIONSHIPS AND TENDENCIES

Ionization potential is an atomic property which can also be used to classify the elements according to their tendencies to be bound either to oxygen or to sulfur. Here, however, it will be applied differently—not as a measure of firmness of binding of electrons, but rather as a measure of the magnitude of the forces associated with the ionized atoms when they react with other atoms or ions, notably those of oxygen or sulfur. Sodium and copper may again serve to illustrate this new application.

It is generally assumed that several of the mineral-forming chemical reactions which take place in a geological environment involve *ionized* atoms. If that is the case, the properties of the participating *ions* will determine the nature of the chemical bond in the mineral produced. One such property is the magnitude of the positive force of attraction associated with a cation, a property sometimes referred to as the *polarizing power* of a cation. In the pair sodium and copper, the magnitude of the positive forces associated with Cu^+ should be greater than those associated with Na^+ because the respective ionization potentials indicate that the outermost electron in copper is more tightly held than in sodium. Accordingly, when Cu^+ interacts with a given anion (O^{2-} or S^{2-} for example), it should exert a greater force on the anion than Na^+. Though the exact nature of such interactions is not fully understood, a fairly simple scheme of events may be assumed for our purpose. The charge distribution of anions such as O^{2-} and S^{2-} may be considered to be spherical. But as these ions come into the positive field of the cation, their symmetrical charge distribution may become asymmetric. Whether, in fact, such distortion (polarization) of the anionic charge distribution does take place or not will depend both on the magnitude of the polarizing power of the cation and on the ease with which the anion can be polarized—its polarizability.

We can quite easily obtain an indication of the magnitude of the polarizing power of a cation through the ionization potential, but though there are suitable techniques, polarizability is not quite so easily measured. For our purpose we need only bear in mind that for anions of a given charge, polarizability will increase with the size of the ion. Thus, in the two series, F^-, Cl^-, Br^-, and I^-, and O^{2-}, S^{2-}, Se^{2-}, and Te^{2-}, radius increases from left to right and so does polarizability. (The two series of anions in question are from Groups VII and VI of the Periodic Table.) For the particular problem at hand we should note that S^{2-} (radius = 1.80 A) is evidently distinctly more polarizable than O^{2-} (radius = 1.40 A).

According to some current theories, increasing polarization-deformation in *either* the cation or the anion leads to an increase in the degree of covalency in the uniting bond; cations are, however, generally less easily polarized than anions, and in our discussion we will consider only the polarizability of the anions. It has been noted (page 33) that the metal-sulfur bond in sulfide minerals is often mainly covalent. According to the above approach this would be due to severe polarization of the sulfur anion. On the other hand, the bond in the oxide minerals including the abundant silicates is mainly ionic, and the less polarizable oxygen anion is evidently not severely polarized. We may anticipate, therefore, that a chalcophile tendency will be shown only by those metals which form with sulfur a bond that has a high degree of covalent character.

Similarly, the essentially lithophile elements are those which form with oxygen bonds that are mainly ionic.

The charge on an ion and its size will influence the nature of a bond because the magnitude of the polarizing power is determined in part by these properties. Accordingly, in the comparisons which are to follow we will in each case consider only cations of the same charge and similar radius magnitude. The cations will be arranged in order of increasing ionization potential. Singly charged cations are considered first.

	Rb^+	K^+	(Na^+)	Tl^+	Ag^+	(Cu^+)	Au^+
Radius (A)	1.45	1.33	0.97	1.44	1.26	0.97	1.37
Ionization potential (eV)	4.2	4.34	5.14	6.1	7.57	7.7	9.22
	No chalcophilic tendency			Chalcophilic tendency			
	I increases		—————————				——————→

The ions Na^+ and Cu^+ have smaller radii than the other ions. They have been placed in brackets and for strict comparison should not be included. As the polarizing power—as indicated by the ionization potential—is increased, a point is reached when the bond becomes sufficiently covalent for the metal to be accepted into sulfide minerals; that is to say, the metal will show a chalcophile tendency. This threshold point is in the vicinity of thallium. The alkali metals show no chalcophile tendency and their bonds with sulfur are ionic rather than covalent. Thallium is on the border line and this interesting element exhibits both distinct lithophile and distinct chalcophile tendencies. Thallium together with elements with comparatively high ionization potentials (~ 6.0 volts or more) are present in many sulfide minerals.

A similar situation holds if we consider the divalent metals. Doubly charged ions of a medium size ($\sim$ 0.65 to 0.80 A) are shown below, arranged in increasing order of the second ionization potential.

	Mg^{2+}	Mn^{2+}	Fe^{2+}	Co^{2+}	Zn^{2+}	Ni^{2+}	Pt^{2+}	Cu^{2+}
Radius (A)	0.65	0.80	0.74	0.72	0.69	0.69	(0.80)	(0.89)
Ionization potential (eV)	15.03	15.64	16.24	17.4	17.94	18.2	19.3	20.3
	I increases	$\longrightarrow$						

Magnesium shows virtually no chalcophilic tendency. Manganese does, and traces of this element are found in several sulfide minerals. The tendency is not marked and manganese like thallium lies on the border line. Cations with a polarizing power greater than that of manganese all show distinct chalcophilic tendencies.

Other cations can be grouped and considered similarly. Generally speaking, such an approach based on some fundamental properties of atoms and on the nature of the chemical bond, provides a reasonably satisfactory explanation of the Goldschmidt classification of the elements.

Before we turn to our next major task, a study of element distribution in igneous rocks, consideration will be given to solid solution, a phenomenon which is of outstanding importance particularly for the rarer elements (Chapter 7), but also for the abundant elements (Chapter 6).

5 SOLID SOLUTION

TO UNDERSTAND WHAT IS MEANT BY SOLID solution we must have some idea both of the atomic structure of solid matter, particularly the structures of the common rock-forming minerals, and of the *size* of an atom. The importance of atomic size is twofold: it both controls the structure of a mineral or other compound, and it determines whether in fact solid solution can occur at all. In the common silicate minerals with which we are concerned, atoms are often in an ionized state; we shall accordingly pay particular attention to the sizes of *ions* rather than of neutral atoms.

The sizes of ions

As a first approximation, ions and atoms of most elements may be taken to be spherical in shape. Thus we may speak of the *radius* of an ion; the unit of measurement is the Angstrom $(1 A = 10^{-8}$ cm$)$. The measurement of ionic radii is based primarily on estimating by means of X rays distances between the centers of ions in a crystalline compound. Given, for example, that the distance between the centers of the Ca^{2+} and O^{2-} ions in a crystal of CaO is 2.41 A and that the radius of O^{2-} is 1.40 A, subtraction of 1.40 A from 2.41 A gives the radius of Ca^{2+} (1.01 A). A list of estimated cationic radii is given in Table 5-1.

Figure 5-1 affords a glimpse of the range and variation of the radii of positively charged metal ions (cations). The radii are drawn to scale and refer to some groups and series in the Periodic Table. The diagram shows clearly that ionic radius decreases as the charge on the cation increases $(Na^+ \rightarrow S^{6+})$ and increases within a vertical column as weight

TABLE 5–1

Ag^+	1.26	Cs^+	1.67	Mg^{2+}	0.65	Sn^{4+}	0.71
Al^{3+}	0.51	Cu^+	0.91	Mn^{2+}	0.80	Sr^{2+}	1.18
Au^+	1.37	Cu^{2+}	0.70	Mn^{3+}	0.66	Th^{4+}	1.02
B^{3+}	0.23	Fe^{2+}	0.74	Mo^{4+}	0.70	Ti^{3+}	0.76
Ba^{2+}	1.34	Fe^{3+}	0.61	Na^+	0.97	Ti^{4+}	0.68
Be^{2+}	0.35	Ga^{3+}	0.57	Nd^{3+}	1.04	Tl^+	1.44
Bi^{3+}	0.96	Ge^{4+}	0.48	Ni^{2+}	0.69	U^{4+}	0.97
Ca^{2+}	1.01	Hf^{4+}	0.78	Pb^{2+}	1.20	V^{3+}	0.74
Cd^{2+}	0.97	Hg^{2+}	1.10	Pb^{4+}	0.85	V^{4+}	0.63
Ce^{3+}	1.07	In^{3+}	0.81	Ra^{2+}	1.43	W^{4+}	0.70
Ce^{4+}	0.94	K^+	1.33	Rb^+	1.45	Y^{3+}	0.95
Co^{2+}	0.72	La^{3+}	1.14	Sc^{3+}	0.81	Zn^{2+}	0.69
Cr^{3+}	0.59	Li^+	0.68	Si^{4+}	0.42	Zr^{4+}	0.79

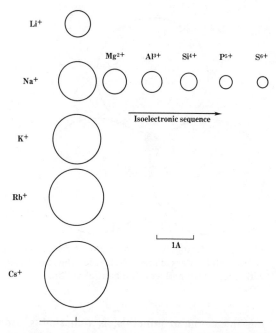

FIG. 5–1 The sizes of cations in the isoelectronic (same electronic structure) series $Na^+ \rightarrow S^{6+}$ and in the alkali metal group $L^+ \rightarrow Cs^+$. Note regular decrease in size as charge increases $(Na^+ \rightarrow S^{6+})$ and regular increase in size with weight $(Li^+ \rightarrow Cs^+)$.

increases $(Li^+ \rightarrow Cs^+)$. The radii of the two abundant anions O^{2-} and S^{2-} are 1.40 A and 1.80 A, respectively, and they are much greater than those of most of the cations.

IONIC STRUCTURES

As a result of intense investigations by means of X rays, it has been possible to obtain a very precise idea of the manner in which ions (or atoms) are arranged in the crystalline solid state of matter. One conclusion from these investigations is clear: the internal structure of crystalline solid matter, includ-

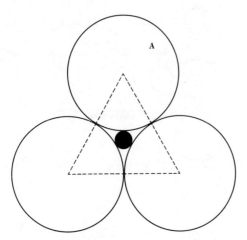

FIG. 5–2   Triangular coordination of anions (A) about central
cation (small dark circle). Note that the anions are in contact
with each other and with the central cation.

ing the common minerals, is remarkably orderly. That is to
say, ions (and atoms) are arranged or grouped in simple
geometrical patterns (triangles, squares, tetrahedra, octahedra,
cubes, etc.). Let us consider this feature further and examine
some possible geometrical arrangements between the large
oxygen anion O^{2-} ($r = 1.40$ A) and some hypothetical cations
of differing radii. As the radius of O^{2-} is much greater than
the radii of the cations, the large oxygen ion will tend to ar-
range itself about the smaller cations. If the cation is really
small, we may imagine the situation depicted in Fig. 5-2.

The large oxygen anions are arranged about the small central cation so that their centers are located at the three corners
of an equilateral triangle. Note that the oxygen ions are in
contact with one another and with the central cation; this
represents a limiting condition. Other limiting conditions will
arise as we increase the radius of the cation. Such conditions

are summarized in Table 5-2 where the size relationships are expressed as ratios; the types of geometrical arrangements and the corresponding *coordinating numbers* are also given.

The coordination number is the number of ions or atoms which lie closest to the central ion (or atom). In other words, the coordination number refers to the number of "nearest neighbors." We speak of threefold (or triangular), fourfold (or tetrahedral or square), sixfold (or octahedral), and eightfold (or cubic) coordination, according to whether the nearest neighboring ions about a central ion are disposed at the corners of a triangle, tetrahedron (or square), octahedron or cube, respectively. These individual polyhedra may be regarded as the units by means of which minerals and crystalline matter in general may be constructed. SiO_4 tetrahedra are of particular importance in this respect, and silicate minerals may be classified according to how the SiO_4 tetrahedra are linked; a few examples are shown in Fig. 5-3. When linked in sheets, structures of the mica type are produced (Fig. 5-4). This is a complex structure when compared, say, with the simple salts of the alkali metals which have the so-called "rocksalt" structure; see any inorganic chemistry text.

TABLE 5–2

Radius ratio (R cation/R anion)		Geometric arrangement of anions about cation	Coordination number of cation
Low limit	High limit		
0.15	0.22	Corners of an equilateral triangle	3
0.22	0.41	Corners of a tetrahedron	4
0.41	0.71	Corners of an octahedron	6
0.73	1.	Corners of a cube	8
1.	1.	Closest packing	12

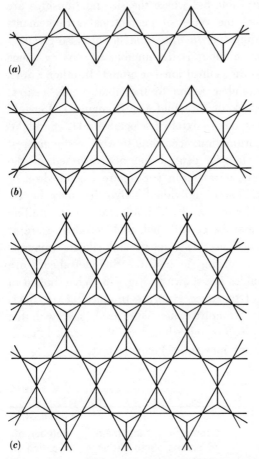

FIG. 5–3   Three types of linking of SiO_4 tetrahedra: (a) each tetrahedron shares two oxygens to form an open chain, as in the pyroxenes, (b) tetrahedra share alternately two and three oxygens, to form double chains, as in the amphiboles, (c) tetrahedra share three oxygens to form open sheets, as in the micas. See also Fig. 5–4. (From "An Introduction to Crystal Chemistry," Fig. 55, p. 232, and Fig. 57, p. 235. By R. C. Evans, Cambridge University Press, 1946.)

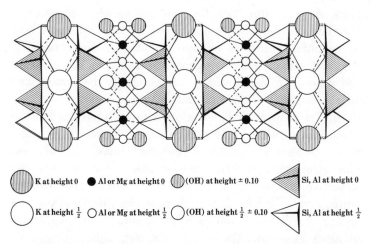

K at height 0 ● Al or Mg at height 0 ▦(OH) at height ± 0.10 ◁ Si, Al at height 0

K at height $\frac{1}{2}$ ○ Al or Mg at height $\frac{1}{2}$ ○ (OH) at height $\frac{1}{2}$ ± 0.10 ◁ Si, Al at height $\frac{1}{2}$

FIG. 5–4 Complex structure of muscovite mica, $(OH)_2KAl_2$ $(Si_3Al)O_{10}$. The structure is based on the sheet arrangement of SiO_4 tetrahedra in Fig. 5–3. Tetrahedra and the various atoms are located at different heights above the plane of the paper. Though it is not clear in the diagram, each Mg^{2+} is surrounded by six oxygens (octahedral coordination) and each K^+ has twelve nearest neighbors of oxygen (twelvefold coordination).

Examples of solid solution and some controlling factors

The composition of the common silicate mineral olivine is normally written

$(Mg,Fe)_2SiO_4$

(Table 3-2, page 29). Both iron and magnesium appear in parentheses because their respective cations, Mg^{2+} and Fe^{2+}, participate in a solid solution relationship; that is to say, Mg^{2+} may replace or substitute for Fe^{2+} (and vice versa) in an octahedral site in the olivine structure. Such replacement takes place quite readily and the two *end-member* components Mg_2SiO_4 and Fe_2SiO_4 form a mixed crystal (solid solution) series. Solid solution is widespread both in the mineral kingdom and in many other inorganic substances, including metals and alloys. Let us consider compounds of the three alkali metals, sodium, potassium, and rubidium together with the Group III element thallium in order to get some guide as to which properties control solid solution. Most of the compounds (halides, sulphates, carbonates, alums, etc.) of these four elements have the same structure, but whereas the respective compounds of potassium, rubidium, and thallium participate in solid solution relationships, those of sodium do not readily enter into such relationships with compounds of other elements. The reason for such behavior suggests itself when we examine the radii of the different cations: $Na^+(0.97 A)$, $K^+(1.33 A)$, $Rb^+(1.45 A)$, and $Tl^+(1.44 A)$. The radii of K^+, Rb^+, and Tl^+ are very similar and these ions readily replace each other, whereas that of Na^+ is some 30 to 40 percent smaller than the radii of the other cations and replacement is more difficult. It is for this reason also that Fe^{2+} readily substitutes for Mg^{2+}; their radii, 0.74 A and 0.65 A, respectively, are quite similar. The control of cation replacement according to radius may be expressed as a rule first enunciated by V. M. Goldschmidt, which in modified form is as follows: "If the radii of two (or more) cations differ by less than 10-20 percent, one cation may substitute readily for another in crystalline matter, provided the cations in question form bonds which are mainly ionic. If the radius difference is moderate (say 20-40 percent) some, but not extensive, substitution may take place." Under these latter circumstances, the extent of substitution will depend largely on the temperature and pressure prevailing in the environment in which a mineral is crystallizing, and to a lesser degree on the structure of the mineral(s) in question. For example, at comparatively high temperatures, some compounds of sodium and potassium, including the two feldspars $NaAlSi_3O_8$ and $KAlSi_3O_8$, may mix extensively. When temperature decreases, some, but not all, of the material in solid solution may unmix (exsolve) giving rise to an intergrowth mixture of the two feldspars, each containing a little of the other in solid solution. In the example of these two compounds, the radius difference of the cations Na^+ and K^+ is about 30 percent.

The importance of structure may be illustrated by examining the distribution of the rare alkali metal cesium in feldspar and biotite mica. Both minerals are found in granite. In these potassium-bearing minerals, Cs^+ (1.67 A) is able to substitute for K^+ (1.33 A), but the disparity in size is considerable and ease of acceptance is evidently controlled significantly by the nature of the two respective structures. In feldspar eight to nine oxygen ions are coordinated to K^+, whereas in biotite the space about K^+ is greater and a dozen oxygen ions surround K^+. It is not surprising therefore that Cs^+ is more readily accepted in the more spacious environment provided by the K^+ site in the biotite structure, and this potassium mineral invariably contains distinctly higher concentrations of cesium than does feldspar.

Though size is usually the most important atomic (or ionic) property, other properties are also significant. Ionic charge is one such. In the examples considered so far, charge has remained the same for each pair (or more) of cations and the question arises as to whether solid solution can take place if the charges differ. We should recall that when we deal with ionic crystals the charges on the cations and anions must balance and the crystal as a whole is electrically neutral. Substitution of a cation of given charge by another of different charge would upset electrostatic balance; because balance must be maintained, substitution by cations with differing charges is very uncommon. The possibility, however, is not ruled out because substitution may take place provided electrostatic balance can be restored in some other way. This may be achieved by a so-called coupled replacement, an excellent example of which is plagioclase feldspar. The two end-members $NaAlSi_3O_8$ and $Ca_2Al_2Si_2O_8$ mix quite freely as the radius (1.01 A) of the doubly charged cation is almost identical to that (0.97 A) of singly charged Na^+; but this replacement becomes possible only because a concomitant replacement, substitution of Al^{3+} by Si^{4+}, takes place elsewhere in the structure. The coupled replacement is therefore

$$Ca^{2+} + Al^{3+} \rightleftharpoons Na^+ + Si^{4+}$$

and electrostatic balance is maintained. Similarly, the two compounds $KAlSi_3O_8$ (potash feldspar) and $BaAlSi_2O_8$ (barium feldspar) can participate in solid solution because the radii of Ba^{2+} and K^+ are almost identical and because electrostatic balance can be maintained by the replacement, $Al^{3+} \rightleftharpoons Si^{4+}$.

In the modified Goldschmidt rule formulated above the proviso is made that the bonds should be "mainly ionic." Coordination affords one principal criterion for classifying the nature of a bond between a metal and nonmetal—if coordination about the metal accords with that of the radius-ratio rule requirements (page 43), the bond may be classed as ionic, but if coordination is lower, the bond is essentially non-ionic. Consider for example, the pairs of cations,

Na^+ and Cu^+
(0.97 A)   ($\sim$0.91 A)

Ca^2 and Cd^{2+}
(1.01 A)   (0.97 A)

In each pair, coordination about the noble-gas ion (Na^+ and Ca^{2+}) is ionic in almost every compound, whereas coordination about Cu^+ and Cd^{2+} is often lower despite the fact that radii are closely similar. (Some Cd^{2+} compounds have ionic co-ordination.) Coordination together with other criteria indicate therefore that whereas the bonds formed by Na^+ and Ca^{2+} in various compounds are essentially ionic, those formed by cadmium and particularly copper are essentially non-ionic. As a consequence, solid solution between compounds of Ca^{2+} and Cd^{2+} is not common and substitution between Na^+ and Cu^+ virtually never takes place to any significant extent.

6 DISTRIBUTION OF THE ABUNDANT ELEMENTS IN IGNEOUS ROCKS

THE ABUNDANT ELEMENTS COMPOSE THE common rock-forming minerals and significantly influence the course of events in the evolution of igneous rocks. Accordingly, it is convenient to consider the abundant elements first as a group, before turning to the distribution of the rarer elements. We shall begin by considering abundance trends in the global averages of the common igneous rocks and then examine trends in rocks from a specific area.

Trends in global averages

A glance through the data on the common igneous rocks (Table 3-1, page 28) shows clearly that several elements are involved in distribution trends as one passes from peridotite (material approximating the composition of the mantle), through basalt and diorite, to the granodiorite and granite of the top of the crust. Consider, for example, the two most abundant constituents, SiO_2 and MgO, which have roughly the same abundance in average peridotite. Whereas SiO_2 tends to increase in the sequence peridotite, basalt, diorite, granodiorite and granite, MgO shows the reverse trend and falls sharply from a concentration of some 40 percent to a magnitude of less than 1 percent. Calcium and iron tend to show trends similar to magnesium, whereas potassium shows a trend similar to silica (SiO_2). These trends involving global averages of large numbers of analyses from many localities on the earth's surface are similar in a general way to those which hold when rocks from one specific area are examined in detail.

Trends in a specific igneous-rock series

For the purpose of examining abundance trends within a series of igneous rocks from one area, the Cascade volcanic province of the northwestern United States has been selected. In this region the volcanic activity, now extinct, was confined to a comparatively recent period in geological history. The principal types of lava flow were basalt, andesite, and rhyolite. Ten rocks have been selected from the Cascade volcanic province and Fig. 6-1 shows a variation diagram in which SiO_2 (horizontal linear scale) is plotted against a few other abundant constituents on the logarithmic vertical scale. A logarithmic scale is often useful if we wish to examine the variation of the concentrations of many elements.

Each constituent in Fig. 6-1 follows a well-defined trend. Because the horizontal scale represents SiO_2, this constituent increases as we pass from the basic rock (basalt) through the intermediate varieties (andesite) and finally to rhyolite. The SiO_2 content of each rock is indicated. The only other con-

FIG. 6–1 Variation diagram for some of the abundant elements in igneous rocks of the Cascade volcanic province in the United States. The relationships are generally typical of most series and groups of igneous rocks. Rock numbers 1, 2, and 3, olivine basalt; 4, basaltic andesite; 5, hypersthene andesite; 6, pyroxene andesite; 7 and 8, dacite; 9 and 10, rhyolite-obsidian.

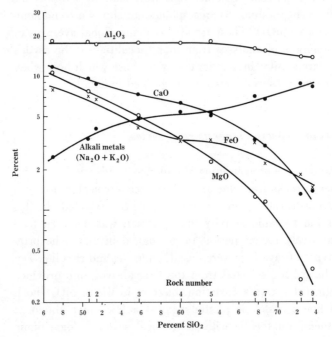

stituent which increases with SiO_2 is the one labeled "alkali metals"; this is $K_2O + Na_2O$. The rate of increase of potash (K_2O), with respect to silica, is generally much greater than that of soda (Na_2O). The distribution trends of the three constituents FeO, CaO, and MgO are inversely related to those of potash and silica in the sequence basalt, andesite, rhyolite. The steepest fall in concentration in these rocks is shown by MgO. The trend followed by Al_2O_3 is distinct from the others as the concentration remains virtually unchanged in six of the rocks and varies only very slightly in the others.

Most of the main features of Fig. 6-1 hold qualitatively also in volcanic rocks of the basalt-andesite-rhyolite association from other areas of the earth's surface. These features occur as well in the plutonic rocks of equivalent composition, gabbro-diorite-granodiorite and granite from specific areas, and in a general way with worldwide averages of related rocks.

Some theoretical considerations

A few of the main features in variation diagrams such as Fig. 6-1 may be explained reasonably well in terms of the melting points and densities of the constituent minerals of the rocks. Because of differences in melting points, a cooling magma will tend to differentiate. That is to say, those minerals with the highest melting points are the first to begin to crystallize. As the temperature continues to fall, other minerals begin to crystallize and precipitate, and the sequence of crystallization-precipitation in the cooling magma in general follows that of the melting points of the silicate minerals. A mineral which precipitates has a composition different from that of the parent magma. The difference may or may not be very great, but in any event, as fractional crystallization (differentiation) proceeds, the composition of the successive crystallizing products and the remaining liquids tend to change in a fairly regular way.

The course of fractional crystallization is not quite so simply dependent on melting point, however. In the first place it may be modified by the fact that those minerals which are the first to precipitate might react to some extent with the remaining liquids. Several minerals may participate in this manner. According to Bowen, a prominent North American petrologist, two principal reaction series may be distinguished when a silicate magma solidifies. Table 6-1 shows these two principal reaction series of minerals which are involved in the development of igneous rocks from a cooling silicate melt. The first-named minerals in the table tend to appear in the earliest fractions of the crystallizing melt. In the one series, several iron-magnesium minerals (ferromagnesians) are the principal participants, whereas in the other, the crystallization reaction relationship involves the plagioclase feldspars.

Crystallization in the plagioclase series begins with the calcium-rich variety bytownite (mp 1450°C) and ends with the sodium-rich variety albite (mp 1100°C). Throughout the whole of this series, variation in composition is smooth because

TABLE 6–1

Discontinuous reaction series	Continuous reaction series
olivines	bytownite (Ca-rich plagioclase)
↘	↙
pyroxenes	labradorite
↘	↙
hornblende	andesine
↘	↙
biotite	oligoclase
	↙
	albite (Na-rich plagioclase)

control is through the process of solid solution (mixed crystal formation). Distinctly more abrupt changes of composition take place in the ferromagnesian series. Within limited regions of this series, referred to sometimes as the discontinuous series, solid solution may, however, take place (olivine and pyroxene), in which case variation of composition will be smoothed. A third reaction series in which sodium and potassium feldspars participate is also believed to exist.

Olivine, with a melting range from 1890°C (Mg_2SiO_4) to 1220°C (Fe_2SiO_4), is commonly one of the first minerals to precipitate from a cooling silicate melt. Because the specific gravity of this mineral is relatively high, it may tend to sink and accumulate toward the bottom of the magma, separating ultimately as a rock enriched in olivine. Convection currents may also tend to influence the composition of a cooling magma. In addition to the general process of fractional crystallization, petrologists speak of "filter press action" and "heaves of a magma" and other descriptive terms when attempting to explain the separation of different igneous rocks and their constituent minerals from a cooling magma. Whatever the precise events may be in a given circumstance, the outcome is that the precipitated products from the fractional crystallization of a silicate melt tend to separate into fairly distinct types, though they usually grade one into the other. Separation may on occasion be so extreme that a rock composed essentially of one mineral only, a monomineralic rock, is formed; anorthosite (mainly calcium plagioclase, anorthite) and dunite (almost entirely olivine) are examples.

In addition to the general process of fractional crystallization, another fractional process, that of fractional melting, may also be important in certain circumstances. The idea is this: solid material, igneous rock for example, may through earth movement in a comparatively unstable region of the crust be forced down to a deep region of the lower crust or upper mantle; there the solid material may begin to melt because temperatures are high. Minerals with the lowest melting points would melt first, and if the conditions were suitable, products from fractional melting might become separated and crystallize elsewhere, giving rise to a differentiated series of rocks. The distribution trends of the elements in igneous rocks which have originated through fractional melting are apparently similar to the trends which arise through processes of fractional crystallization.

7 ELEMENT ASSOCIATION IN IGNEOUS ROCKS AND MINERALS

THE IMPORTANCE OF SOLID SOLUTION relationships for controlling element distribution, particularly that of the rarer elements, has been noted (page 38). It has also been demonstrated (Chapter 5) that such relationships depend primarily on atomic or ionic size. Now we must demonstrate the importance of size (expressed as the ionic radius) in the control of element distribution, with particular emphasis on the rarer elements. We shall not consider individual elements one at a time; instead, we shall select various groups of elements, abundant and rare, whose cations have similar radii and study their geochemical distribution relationships. The inference is that if the cations of some given elements do have similar ionic radii, their distribution behavior in igneous rocks and minerals should be similar; such elements would be geochemically associated; they are said to be geochemically coherent.

Though our primary object will be to test the importance of ionic radius, three secondary aims guide this investigation: first, to demonstrate that the nature of the bond may also affect the geochemical behavior of elements in igneous rocks and minerals; second, to show that different mineral structures may also play a role. The third factor which may influence element distribution will not require detailed consideration. It arises from the fact that minerals are not perfect crystalline compounds. Cracks and other voids may abound in some minerals, and certain elements may deposit in the cavities; these elements are not, therefore, occupants of structure sites of the mineral.

Let us now consider the geochemical association of some selected groups of elements in order to test the importance of ionic radius; we shall begin with groups of univalent elements, and thereafter, consider other groups of elements.

Some groups of univalent elements

POTASSIUM AND RUBIDIUM

The two heavy alkali metals potassium and rubidium will serve as the first example. Potassium is an abundant element and forms common minerals of its own, notably feldspar and mica, whereas rubidium is comparatively rare. It is about $\frac{1}{250}$ as abundant as potassium. The radii of the two singly charged cations K^+ and Rb^+ are very similar, namely 1.33 A and 1.45 A, respectively. Figure 7-1 displays the relationship between these two elements as we pass from the common silicate meteorites (chondrites) through various types of common terrestrial igneous rocks, including a rather special group which is referred to as the "small volume residuals," aplite veins, certain small outcrops of granite and pegmatites, rocks which may be regarded as representing the residuum (mother liquor fraction) resulting from the fractional crystallization of large volumes of molten silicates. The diagram shows first that aside from this special group of rocks the relationship is linear and has unit slope. There is little or no significant fractionation, therefore, and the ratio of potassium to rubidium (approxi-

FIG. 7–1 The relationship between potassium and rubidium in common meteorites (chondrites) and common igneous rocks. The slope of the straight line is unity, showing therefore that the ratio K/Rb remains virtually unchanged throughout all the rocks and meteorites which have been investigated.

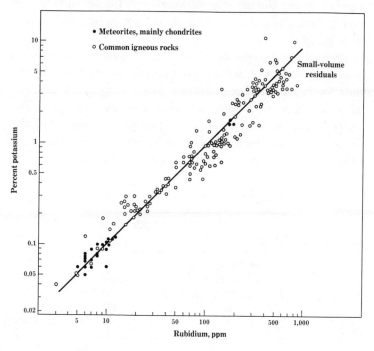

mately 250 to 1) remains virtually unchanged until we reach the small volume residuals. It is of particular interest to observe that the magnitude of this ratio remains substantially the same as we pass from the meteorites to the terrestrial rocks; the importance of this observation has been noted (Chapter 2). You will recall (Chapter 3) that abundant potassium forms several common minerals found in igneous rocks, notably feldspar and mica. The structures of these minerals evidently accept the much rarer rubidium because Rb^+ is able to substitute for K^+; such substitution takes place so freely, in fact, that rubidium never forms a mineral of its own, a situation which may be contrasted with that of cesium (page 63). A distinct enrichment of rubidium, relative to potassium, does however take place in the "small volume residuals." Rubidium reaches its maximum concentration ($\sim$ 1.5 percent) in the rare potassium-lithium mica lepidolite, a mineral which occurs in pegmatites.

Preferential acceptance of Rb^+ into potassium minerals, as opposed to those of sodium for example, is illustrated by the data in Table 7-1. Each of the separate constituent minerals of a specimen of granite was separated and analyzed. The analysis showed that the concentration of rubidium in biotite mica and potash feldspar is considerably greater than in the other minerals. The comparatively low rubidium concentration

TABLE 7-1

Mineral	Rb content, ppm
Biotite mica	900
Potash feldspar	300
Plagioclase feldspar	20
Hornblende	50
Quartz	1

in plagioclase feldspar is worthy of note; it is evidently due to the fact that the large cation Rb^+ (1.45 A) does not easily substitute for Na^+ (0.97 A) because of the considerable difference in size between the two ions.

Table 7-1 reveals a second feature of the rubidium distribution; namely, a higher rubidium concentration in biotite than in potash feldspar. This feature is quite characteristic and illustrates the importance of the structure of a mineral for controlling element distribution. Rb^+ readily replaces K^+ in both feldspar and mica structures, but as the mica structure is in a sense "roomier" than the feldspar structure, the relatively large Rb^+ is more easily accommodated in mica (see also page 47).

POTASSIUM AND CESIUM

The relationship between cesium, the heaviest alkali metal, and potassium is similar, in a general way, to that of rubidium and potassium. Again the radii of the two are similar, though by no means so close. The radius of Cs^+ (1.67 A) is distinctly larger than that of K^+ (1.33 A). This difference probably accounts for the fact that, compared with the potassium-rubidium relationship, that between cesium and potassium is not nearly so well-developed. Thus, for example, whereas the ratio K/Rb remains fairly steady in granites and related rocks, that of K/Cs shows a much greater variation in the same rocks. This relationship is shown clearly in Fig. 7-2. It must be pointed out at once that the diagrams of Fig. 7-2 refer actually to sedimentary rocks (mainly shales) and not to igneous rocks. The sedimentary rock diagrams have been used for illustration here merely because the data were available in a particularly convenient form; the relationship in igneous rocks is quite similar. The scatter of points in the Cs-K diagram is markedly greater than in the Rb-K diagram.

Enrichment of cesium relative to potassium in "small volume

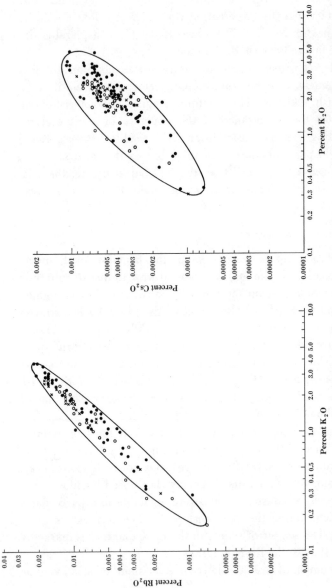

FIG. 7-2   The relationship between potassium and rubidium and potassium and cesium in common sediments. Note that the K-Rb relationship is closer than that of K-Cs. These features apply in general also to igneous rocks.

residuals" is much greater than that of rubidium. Enrichment is in fact occasionally so marked that despite its rarity, cesium may sometimes form a mineral of its own whereas rubidium does not. The cause of the relatively poor Cs-K coherence when compared with that of Rb-K is clearly due to ionic radii differences. The example is perhaps the best we have to illustrate the effect of ionic radii differences.

RUBIDIUM AND THALLIUM

Both potassium and cesium are alkali metals, and they have the same electronic structure. Let us consider another pair of elements in which electronic structures differ; one element, rubidium, is again an alkali metal, but the other, thallium, is a member of Group III in the Periodic Table. We have noted (page 37) that thallium may be univalent and that the radius of Tl^+ (1.44 A) is identical to that of Rb^+. Thallium is a very rare element with an abundance about $\frac{1}{200}$ that of rubidium. Instead of comparing the Rb-Tl distribution relationship in common rocks as in the K-Rb example, we shall instead examine the relationship in individual minerals (Fig. 7-3). A great variety of silicate mineral types are represented. Most are potassium minerals and it is assumed that both Rb^+ and Tl^+ are able to substitute for K^+ in these minerals. The range in concentration is large (approximately 1,000) and throughout this range the Rb-Tl relationship seems to be approximately linear, though the scatter of points is quite large.

Rubidium reaches its maximum concentration in lepidolite mica (page 60), and it is worth noting in Fig. 7-3 that thallium likewise reaches its maximum concentration (for a silicate mineral) in the same type of mica. This is a truly elegant illustration of the control of ionic radius. Bear in mind that minerals are formed by complicated processes, and that those under consideration have come from the four corners of our planet.

FEATURES OF THE DISTRIBUTION OF LITHIUM

The geochemical distribution of the lightest alkali metal, lithium, is of unusual interest because this element tends to follow a well-defined path of its own in contrast to those several elements which are often associated with other elements. In fact, the distribution of lithium is almost entirely distinct from

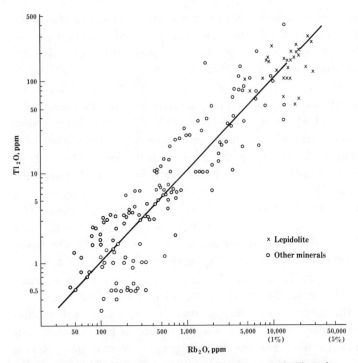

Fig. 7–3 The relationship between rubidium and thallium in 167 minerals, mostly potassic varieties. Though the spread of points is considerable, the Rb-Tl relationship is quite well-developed over the whole of the 1,000-fold range of concentration that is involved. Note maximum enrichment both of thallium and of rubidium in the lepidolite micas.

the other alkali metals. These characteristics arise from the fact that not only is Li^+ distinctly smaller (radius $= 0.68$ A) than the other alkali metal cations, but it is the smallest of all singly charged cations. This places Li^+ in a category of its own: unlike the larger cations which occur in eightfold (or higher) coordination in silicate minerals, coordination about Li^+ is invariably different and lower (sixfold). The "smallness" of the lithium ion will be emphasized in our discussion of some aspects of lithium distribution, but lithium permits the illustration of another important factor in geochemical distribution—charge difference. The data which we first consider are those of the lithium contents of muscovite mica and "side-by-side" occurring specimens of feldspar (soda or potash) from eight pegmatites (Table 7-2) from Namaqualand, South Africa.

Evidently for each "side-by-side" occurring pair of mica and feldspar, lithium concentrates strongly in the mica only. This is generally true. Whereas Li^+ cannot find a home in the feldspar structure because it cannot replace the constituent ions (K^+, Na^+, Ca^{2+}, Al^{3+} and Si^{4+}), it readily does so in the

TABLE 7-2

Pegmatite no.	Li content, ppm	
	Mica	Feldspar
1	70	< 5
2	140	< 5
3	6,000	< 5
4	4,000	8
5	600	< 5
6	5,000	< 5
7	6,000	< 5
8	150	< 5

mica structure. Because of its size ($r = 0.68$ A), it cannot replace one of the abundant alkali cations (Na^+ or K^+) in mica, but may readily be accepted into the octahedral structure sites occupied by the cations Mg^{2+}, Fe^{2+}, and also Al^{3+} which are present in the mica structure but not in the feldspar structure. A situation similar to that of the mica-feldspar pairs in pegmatites holds if individual minerals in an igneous rock are separated and analyzed: the highest lithium concentrations by far are found in the micas whereas feldspar invariably contains very low concentrations, usually about a ppm or less. If hornblende, a ferromagnesian mineral, is present in the igneous rock, several ppm of lithium will probably be present in this mineral because of the ability of Li^+ to replace Fe^{2+} and Mg^{2+} in its structure.

The possibility of Li^+ replacing the medium-sized (radii $\sim$ 0.7 A) cations Mg^{2+} and Fe^{2+} raises an interesting question about the fate of lithium in a series of igneous rocks. It will be recalled that the ferromagnesium minerals, olivine and pyroxene, are abundant in ultrabasic and basic rocks. If Li^+ were to be readily accepted into the structures of these minerals, the lithium content might tend to decrease as one passed from distinctly basic rock types to acid varieties. The reverse tends to be the case, however. Ultrabasic rocks contain the lowest concentration (a couple of ppm or so) and granitic rocks the highest (average, 30 ppm); the average for basaltic rocks is about 10 ppm. The same type of relationship holds for rocks from igneous-rock series from specific regions. Magnesium and iron concentrations tend to decrease in a series from ultrabasic to granitic rocks, and the lithium distribution in igneous rocks tends to be inversely related to that of magnesium and iron.

The reason for this inverse relationship appears to lie in the fact that whereas Li^+ is singly charged, the cation Mg^{2+} and Fe^{2+} each carry a charge of two. It seems that when cations of differing charge compete for a given structure site in a silicate mineral that is growing from a cooling silicate melt, ions with the higher charge tend to be accepted preferentially because the magnitude of the positive forces associated with these ions will be greater than those associated with the less strongly charged ions. Accordingly, the singly charged ion Li^+ tends to be rejected from the ferromagnesian minerals which crystallize early in a differentiated series of rocks, and lithium tends to concentrate in the rocks which represent fairly late products in the series, the intermediate and acidic rocks.

Although this explanation for the inverse relationship between lithium on the one hand and magnesium and iron on the other may be correct, there is another point which arises from a difference in charge and which may also cause lithium enrichment. Though Li^+ may be easily accepted into the *mica* structure, the olivine and pyroxene structures might not readily accept Li^+, because electrostatic balance cannot be maintained by a coupled replacement elsewhere in the structure (page 48). Rejection of Li^+ for this reason would naturally lead to an enrichment of lithium as described above.

Metals with an oxidation state greater than two

The preceding examples have involved univalent elements. We now consider elements whose atoms occur in higher oxidation states beginning with the trivalent elements, aluminum and gallium.

ALUMINUM AND GALLIUM

After oxygen and silicon, aluminum is the most abundant element in the earth's crust. A high proportion of several of the common igneous rocks is composed of aluminum-bearing minerals, notably the feldspars and micas. In contrast, gallium is very rare—approximately $\frac{1}{1,000}$ the abundance of aluminum —but apparently finds a ready home in all aluminum minerals because the radius (0.57 A) of the cation Ga^{3+} is quite similar to that (0.50 A) of Al^{3+}. In this respect, laboratory experiment has shown that the two feldspars, $KAlSi_3O_8$ and $KGaSi_3O_8$, form a mixed crystal pair. The Al-Ga relationship is so close that the ratio of the two elements remains relatively uniform as we pass from one rock type to another and throughout an igneous rock series. The close control through ionic radius of the destiny of gallium may be quite strikingly illustrated in another way. The dispersion of aluminum in some common igneous rocks (granitic and basaltic types, for example) is usually much smaller than that of the other elements; because of the close association between aluminum and the so-called trace element gallium, the dispersion of gallium is far smaller than that of the great majority of the other trace elements (Chapter 8).

SILICON AND GERMANIUM

If we move horizontally one step across the Periodic Table from Al and Ga, we come to Si and Ge, respectively. Silicon is the most abundant of all the metal elements, and it is of interest to bear in mind that we are dealing with silicate rocks and minerals. The abundance of the trace metal germanium is only a very small fraction ($\sim \frac{1}{10,000}$) of that of silicon, but these traces are easily accommodated by the silicate minerals because the radii of Si^{4+} and Ge^{4+} are very similar, 0.42 A and 0.47 A, respectively. The ratio Si/Ge varies only slightly in the various silicates.

There may, however, be other factors that influence the Si/Ge relationship. Highly charged cations such as Si^{4+} and Ge^{4+} tend to bind the surrounding oxygens quite tightly into units or complexes. It may be the sizes of these condensed complexes which in part control behavior and distribution, rather than the sizes of the "bare" cations Si^{4+} and Ge^{4+}.

Much is heard these days of the so-called transistors. Germanium metal is one principal constituent of many a transistor crystal. But in view of the extraordinarily low concentrations of germanium in silicates, how is it extracted and processed into the pure metal? Although the great bulk of the germanium in the earth's crust is tied up in the abundant silicate minerals, germanium has distinct chalcophilic tendencies so that it is found highly concentrated in some rare sulfide minerals from which it is quite easily recovered.

THE RARE EARTH ELEMENTS

The examples considered so far have all involved small numbers of elements, usually two. In the example which follows, 14 elements participate; these are the rare earths. They belong to Group III in the Periodic Table and are usually taken to include all elements from lanthanum to lutetium. Another Group III element, yttrium, because of a similarity of properties, is sometimes considered together with the Rare Earths. (Hereafter, for the sake of brevity, these elements will be referred to as the R.E.s.)

The chemical properties of the R.E.s are very similar, a characteristic which arises from three main facts: most of these elements have only one principal oxidation state (three); their cationic radii are similar, ranging from about 1.15 A for La^{3+} down to about 0.9 A for Lu^{3+}; finally, the ionization potentials and electronegativities are of the same general magnitude. Because of these three similar characteristics, the nature of the bonds which each of these elements forms with oxygen is of the same general kind.

As we have done heretofore (Chapter 2), let us assume that the earth originated from cosmic substance with a composition corresponding fairly closely to that of average chondrite meteorites. To what extent, then, has the R.E. abundance pattern in the starting material, as indicated by meteorite data, been preserved in the common types of crustal igneous rocks?

An impression of the meteorite abundances of all the elements was given in Fig. 2-1 (page 14). The even-odd effect (the rule of Oddo and Harkins, page 15) and other abundance features of the R.E.s are revealed more clearly when examined on a bigger scale (Fig. 7-4). Apart from the even-odd effect, a second feature is apparent: abundance falls as atomic number (La to Lu) increases. These features may be compared with those holding for R.E. abundance in the common terrestrial rocks, basalt and granite (Fig. 7-4). For both these common terrestrial rock types, the even-odd abundance relationship is again evident and *qualitatively* the same general abundance trend is maintained. The basaltic abundance pattern resembles the chondrite pattern much more closely than does the granite pattern. It is of interest to note that the rate of fall of abundance (La → Lu) tends to steepen in the sequence, chondrite → basalt → granite. This effect may be demonstrated also by relating the ratios of the concentration of each rare earth in granite to basalt; this is shown in Fig. 7-5. The ratio falls quite regularly from La → Lu.

Evidently, similarity in ionic radius has played a major role in holding the R.E.s together, but the small differences in radii are nevertheless significant. Presumably they account for these changes in the abundance trends. A far greater variation in R.E. abundance patterns is apparent if rather than rocks specific R.E. minerals are considered. Numerous R.E. minerals are known. Many occur in pegmatites. Although a study of the abundance relationships in these rare minerals is fascinating, our emphasis here is on element distributions in the most abundant rocks and minerals of the earth's crust.

The other comparatively rare elements, rubidium, cesium, thallium, lithium, gallium, and germanium, which have been considered in this chapter have been accommodated, through cationic substitution, in the host structures of minerals of certain common elements. Where do the R.E.s find a home in rocks such as basalt and granite? The abundant element

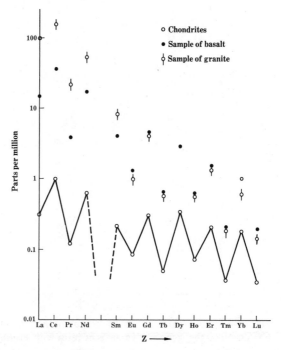

FIG. 7–4   Rare earth abundance patterns in chondritic meteorites, basalt, and granite. Whereas the drop in abundance
with atomic number is slight in the chondrites, the fall is quite
sharp in the specimen of granite; the trend (abundance vs.
atomic number) in the basalt specimen is intermediate between that of the average chondrite and the specimen of
granite.

calcium seems to play a key role. It is a principal constituent
of the common mineral plagioclase feldspar; because the radius
of Ca^{2+} (1.01 A) is similar in magnitude to the radii of the
R.E. cations, the possibility of substitution of Ca^{2+} by R.E.
cations arises. Plagioclase feldspar could, then, act as a host
mineral for the R.E.s. This feldspar is a principal constituent

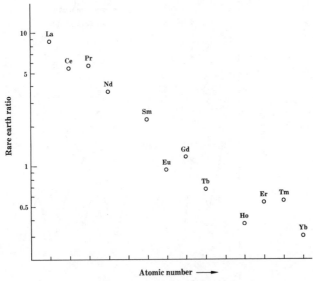

FIG. 7–5   Rare earth ratios in a granite and a specimen of basalt. Note the general decrease in ratio with atomic number.

of the common igneous rock basalt, and if the R.E.s were readily accommodated in the plagioclase structure, their concentration would presumably decrease on passing from basaltic rocks to granitic rocks. The reverse is, however, the case. In fact, the R.E. concentration in granites is sometimes far greater than in basalt. The probable reason is that the plagioclase structure does not readily facilitate a substitution of a trebly charged R.E. cation for a doubly charged calcium ion because charge balance can evidently not be easily restored by a coupled replacement of the type described on page 48. Hence, the R.E.s tend to concentrate in acid rocks such as granite which are supposed to represent—at least at a first approximation—the end products of fractional crystallization of a silicate melt of basaltic composition (page 53).

We have not yet satisfactorily answered the question as to where the R.E.s find a home in the common igneous rocks. Because of the difficulty of separating minerals from basalt, we are still unfortunately much in the dark about these rocks. Perhaps the *small* amounts of the R.E.s present in them are located mainly in the plagioclase feldspar. But granites are coarse-grained rocks, and the constituent minerals may be separated quite easily. Table 7-3 gives some data on the R.E. contents of some individual minerals which have been separated from a specimen of granite.

It is quite clear that the R.E.s are concentrated in some of the *accessory* minerals, notably monazite. These accessory minerals are quite rare and in this respect we may contrast the distribution of the R.E.s with the distribution of the other comparatively rare elements. Whereas the other rare elements (Rb, Cs, Tl, Li, Ga, etc.) are readily accepted into the host structures of common silicate minerals such as feldspar and mica, rejection of the R.E.s by these minerals leads to R.E. concentration, sometimes to a very high degree, in minerals which may be present in minute amounts. It may be noted,

TABLE 7–3

Mineral	Rare earth concentration, percent	Percent proportion of total R.E. content
Feldspar	0.01	29.2
Biotite mica	0.06	8.9
Garnet	0.03	0.6
Apatite	0.5	2.2
Monazite	50.	58.5

nevertheless (Table 7-3), that although the R.E. concentration in feldspar is very low ($\sim$ 0.01 percent), the proportion of the total R.E. content carried by this abundant mineral is high (29 percent).

URANIUM AND THORIUM

Spectacular developments in nuclear technology have focused attention on the two rare and radioactive elements, uranium and thorium. Thorium is the more abundant of the two; the ratio Th/U averages at 3 to 4 in the common meteorites and in the common igneous rocks of the crust.

The distribution trends of these two elements in the common igneous rocks are similar. This stems mainly from two facts; both elements have characteristic oxidation states of four, and the radii of the cations U^{4+} and Th^{4+} are similar, namely 0.97 A and 1.02 A, respectively.

The concentrations of uranium and thorium tend to increase as we pass from basic rocks (ave U = 0.6 ppm; ave Th = 2.5 ppm) to acid varieties such as granite, where magnitudes of 5 ppm U and 15 to 20 ppm Th are typical. This trend is similar to that shown by several of the other elements discussed so far. The reason lies principally in the fact that large and highly charged U^{4+} and Th^{4+} are not readily accommodated in the structures of the common rock-forming minerals. Like the R.E.s, uranium and thorium tend to concentrate in the accessory minerals of igneous rocks, monazite, sphene, zircon, apatite, and alanite, for example. Of these, zircon ($ZrSiO_4$) is one of the most common and also the most interesting because of its use for estimating geological age by means of the radioactivity of uranium and thorium (page 3). In zircon, U^{4+} and Th^{4+} are able to replace Zr^{4+} (r = 0.80 A).

Figure 7-6 gives a good indication of the distribution of uranium and thorium in zircon from granites. The concentra-

tion of each element varies quite widely and it is interesting to
note that the thorium concentration shows a greater "spread"
than the uranium concentration. (It might be noted also that
the horizontal scale is logarithmic; the significance of using
such a scale is discussed in Chapter 8.)

Covalency and crystal-field effects

The importance of ionic radius is clear in each of the examples we have considered, but in those which follow, radius
plays a lesser role; in fact, for some elements radius appears
to have very little significance indeed. The examples which
we are about to consider fall into two categories. The first
includes several nontransitional B-subgroup elements of the
Periodic Table (the so-called 18-electron elements), and the
second is composed entirely of transition elements, notably
some of the third transition group.

Fig. 7–6 Frequency distribution diagram of the concentration of uranium and of thorium in zircon, a common accessory
mineral of granite. The spread of concentration of thorium is
distinctly greater than that of uranium.

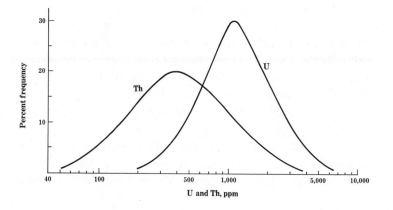

Elements belonging to the first group possess either chalcophile or siderophile tendencies; Ag, Au, Cd, Hg, and, to a lesser extent Zn, are examples. The fact that these elements are either chalcophile or siderophile does not mean that they have concentrated to such an extent in either sulfide minerals or the earth's core that virtually nothing is left of them to go into the silicates. Distinct traces of these elements may be found in silicate minerals, but their distribution patterns simply do not "follow the rules." For example, the radius of Ag^+ (1.26 A) is very similar to that of K^+ (1.33 A), yet there appears to be no close association as in the examples of potassium and rubidium or rubidium and thallium. Potassium minerals are not enriched in silver, nor in gold for that matter, despite the fact that the radius of Au^+ (1.37 A) is almost identical with that of K^+. The pair calcium-cadmium likewise show little or no geochemical coherence despite a close similarity in radii of Ca^{2+} (1.01 A) and Cd^{2+} (0.97 A). One might expect an enrichment of cadmium in calcium minerals, but this is rarely the case.

The recalcitrance of these elements to associate is reasonably well-understood. First, the coordination of the oxygen anion about the cations Ag^+, Au^+, Cd^{2+}, Hg^{2+}, and Zn^{2+} is often lower than that predicted by the ionic radius ratio rules (page 43). Accordingly, the substitution of these cations for the abundant cations (K^+, Ca^{2+}, Mg^{2+}, etc.) in their respective minerals is hindered. Second, there is the problem of the nature of the bond. The presence of a high degree of covalency also hinders substitution. Whereas the cations (K^+, Ca^{2+}, Mg^{2+}, etc.) of the common elements form distinctly ionic bonds with O^{2-}, bonds between Ag, Au, Hg and Zn, and oxygen are distinctly covalent.

The behavior of a second group of elements cannot be explained in terms of size, bond disposition, or the covalency effect we have just considered. These "unusual" elements belong to the so-called Transition Group of the Periodic Table, and they include Ti, V, Cr, Mn, Fe, Co, Ni, and elements belonging to the platinum group. For the purpose of our discussion, we shall choose nickel because it illustrates "unusual" behavior almost to an extreme.

The stable oxidation state of nickel in a geological environment is two, and because the radius of Ni^{2+} (0.68 A) is similar to that of Mg^{2+} and Fe^{2+}, a close geochemical association between nickel and the abundant elements magnesium and iron might be anticipated. In support of this expectation, there is the fact that laboratory experiments show that a nickel olivine, Ni_2SiO_4, can be prepared which forms a solid solution with the magnesium olivine, Mg_2SiO_4; in other words, Ni^{2+} may replace Mg^{2+} and presumably also Fe^{2+}. It is true that the vast amount of geochemical data shows clearly that nickel does find a natural home in the silicates of magnesium and iron, but problems arise when we begin to examine the behavior of nickel in an igneous rock series.

Figure 7-7 shows a variation diagram in which nickel, together with a few other elements included for comparison, is related to SiO_2 in a series of nine igneous rocks from the Lassen Peak region, northwestern United States. We may recall that in variation diagrams of this kind (see Fig. 6-1), the magnesium concentration tends to decrease regularly and steeply as SiO_2 increases. This feature is apparent also in the Lassen Peak rocks. The same general feature is shown by nickel, but to a much more marked degree. This element is highly concentrated in the magnesium-rich rocks which are the first to form from a cooling silicate melt, but concentration falls sharply in the acid rocks (high SiO_2). This characteristic feature of nickel (even more marked in chromium), is common in various suites of igneous rocks, volcanic and plutonic, and cannot be explained by size, bond, or covalency effect without further analysis. According to current thought,

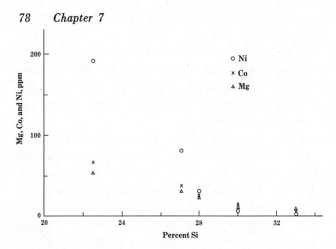

Fig. 7–7 Variation diagram for nickel, magnesium, and cobalt in igneous rocks from the Lassen Peak area in the United
States. The sharp fall in the nickel concentration is a striking
and characteristic feature of this element. (Mg is × $\frac{1}{100}$ the
actual amount.)

bonds associated with nickel can be "stabilized" in rather a
special way; because of such stabilization nickel is preferentially accepted into the rocks which are the first to crystallize
from a cooling melt. The stabilization itself is ascribed to
the phenomenon of "crystal field splitting," a property which
takes us into a specialized section of theoretical chemistry.
For this discussion of the importance of various atomic properties in controlling element distribution, suffice it to note
again that the Transition Group elements are indeed "unusual"
from the standpoint of their distribution.

8 STATISTICS OF ELEMENT DISTRIBUTIONS IN IGNEOUS ROCKS

THOUGH WE HAVE SPOKEN OF SPECIFIC types of rocks and minerals—granite, basalt, potash-feldspar, biotite mica, and so on—these generalized types rarely possess an exact composition, as compared for example with many man-made chemical substances. The average SiO_2 content of basalt is 48.5 percent (Table 3-1), but the range is from a little over 40 percent to a little over 55 percent. Composition may vary widely or hardly at all; the degree of variation will depend both on the rock or mineral in question and on the particular element under consideration.

The extent to which the concentration of an element varies is itself interesting, but we are also concerned with how the concentration varies. In other words, what is the statistical nature of the distribution of element-concentration in a given type of rock? We shall look at both these aspects of variation of composition in specific geological materials. The non-mathematician need have no fear of what follows. This significant aspect of geochemistry, which falls very much within the scope of our general study of element distributions, may be handled for the most part with only an elementary knowledge of mathematics. Where the mathematics becomes tricky, illustrations in the form of diagrams speak for themselves.

Geological examples of the Normal distribution

Consider the distribution of silica, the most abundant of all constituents in the earth's crust, in the two volcanic rocks rhyolite and basalt. A frequency distribution diagram is shown in Fig. 8-1. Each distribution is symmetrical and bell-shaped; in appearance each is typical of the well-known Normal distribution. There are several other types of statistical distribution, but the Normal is particularly useful because the statistical handling and presentation of data are greatly facilitated if normality can be assumed.

Mathematically, the expression for a normal curve looks quite formidable, thus

$$y = \frac{1}{s \sqrt{2\pi}} \, e^{\frac{-(x - \bar{x})^2}{2s^2}}$$

y is the height of the curve at any point along the scale of x, the variate or variable quantity; $\bar{x}$ is the average or arithmetic mean. The average $(\bar{x})$ is a parameter for a given series of observations (48.5 percent SiO_2 in basalt) and so is s, the standard deviation. The standard deviation is a measure of the dispersion of the observations and is estimated by means of the relationship,

$$s = \pm \sqrt{\frac{\Sigma \, d^2}{n-1}}$$

where n is the number of observations and d the deviation of each individual value from the average $(\overline{x})$.

According to Normal Law statistics, two-thirds of a given series of observations should fall within $+ 1$ standard deviation and -1 standard deviation of the average $(\overline{x})$. This corresponds to two-thirds of the area under a normal curve, as indicated for the case of SiO_2 in basalt by the cross-hatching in Fig. 8-1. In the example of SiO_2 in basalt, s calculates at ± 3.3 percent, and, accordingly, two-thirds of the basalts should have SiO_2 values falling between $48.5 - 3.3$ percent and $48.5 + 3.3$ percent; that is, between 45.2 and 51.8 percent SiO_2. Another limit which is sometimes used corresponds to the range, $x \pm 2s$; these are the so-called 95 percent limits. In the example of SiO_2 in basalt, $2s = 6.6$ percent, and the 95 percent limits are 41.9 percent SiO_2 (lower limit) and 55.1 percent SiO_2 (upper limit).

The standard deviation is an absolute value, and for some purposes it is convenient to employ a measure of dispersion that is relative rather than absolute, namely the standard deviation expressed as a percent. This quantity is commonly referred to as the coefficient of variation (c) though it may also be called relative deviation, or, more simply, percent spread. c is given by the relationship

$$c = \frac{s}{\overline{x}} \times 100$$

(It so happens that the variate (SiO_2) in our example, is expressed in units of percent, but this is purely fortuitous.)

Inspection of Fig. 8-1 shows that the basalt and rhyolite

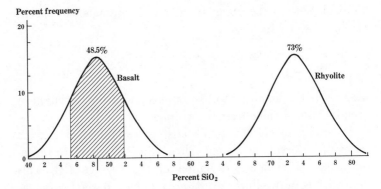

FIG. 8–1   Frequency distribution diagrams of SiO₂ in the flow rocks, basalt and rhyolite. Both distributions are symmetrical and bell-shaped, and in general appearance are typical of a Normal Distribution. The cross-hatched area in the basalt distribution represents two-thirds of the total area under the curve and corresponds to the two-thirds limits; ± the standard deviation.

curves appear to be very similar; indeed calculation shows that the respective standard deviations are identical (± 3.3 percent SiO_2). The curves are, however, displaced and the arithmetic means differ considerably (48.5 percent SiO_2 in basalt and 73 percent SiO_2 in rhyolite). Therefore, c will differ and according to the above expression, calculates at ± 6.6 percent for basalt and ± 4.7 percent for rhyolite. Thus, although the *absolute* "spread" is the same in basalt and rhyolite, the *relative* "spread" is greater in basalt than in rhyolite.

In these calculations normality has been assumed. Rarely, however, does a series of observations conform *precisely* with the Normal distribution, or any of the other distributions set up by mathematicians. But if the Normal distribution is closely approximated, normality may be assumed. Inspection of frequency distribution diagrams (histograms) may permit a preliminary judgment as to whether a distribution is likely to approach normality or not, but a more rigorous and quite simple test can be carried out by means of probability paper. One scale is linear but the other is so constructed that if observations are normally distributed linearity will be obtained when the *cumulative percent frequency* is related to the variate (SiO_2 in the examples under consideration).

Calculation of cumulative percent frequency is illustrated by the data on SiO_2 in 401 specimens of basalt of worldwide occurrence (Table 8-1). The first column gives the interval (1 percent) that has been chosen and the second the number

TABLE 8–1

Interval percent SiO_2	Number of observations per interval	Percent frequency per interval	Cumulative percent frequency
39–40	2	0.50	0.50
40–41	3	0.75	1.25
41–42	5	1.25	2.50
42–43	10	2.50	5.
43–44	24	6.	11.
44–45	24	6.	17.
45–46	33	8.25	25.25
46–47	34	8.50	33.75
47–48	46	11.50	45.25
48–49	47	11.75	57.
49–50	43	10.75	67.75
50–51	32	8.	75.75
51–52	40	10.	85.75
52–53	28	7.	92.75
53–54	14	3.50	96.25
54–55	7	1.75	98.
55–56	5	1.25	99.25
56–57	3	0.50	99.75
> 57	1	0.25	100.

of observations falling within that interval. The third column gives the percentage frequency per interval. (The data in either column two or three could be used for constructing frequency distribution diagrams.) Cumulative percent frequency is given in the last column and is obtained by adding the successive values in column three.

Probability paper tests for the normality of SiO_2 in basalt (data listed in Table 8-1) are shown in Fig. 8-2. The standard deviation may be estimated by noting on the percent SiO_2 scale, the values corresponding to intercepts between the fitted straight line and vertical line drawn through the horizontal

FIG. 8–2 Probability paper test for normality of SiO_2 in 401 specimens of basalt. The straight line accommodates the plotted points very well and the distribution may therefore be regarded as Normal.

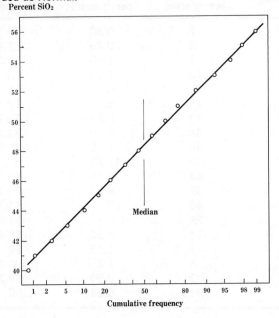

Percent SiO_2

Cumulative frequency

scale at the 17th and 83d percentiles. These percentiles correspond to the $-\frac{1}{3}$ and $+\frac{1}{3}$ limits on either side of the 50th percentile, the median value.

Skew distributions (general)

Distribution of SiO_2 in basalt and rhyolite provided examples of statistically Normal distribution. Two further questions now arise: (1) Does SiO_2 follow the same type of statistical distribution in other types of igneous rock? (2) Do other elements also tend in general to follow Normal distribution? The answer to the first question is a decided "no." For example, in granites the SiO_2 distribution appears to be assymmetrical and *negatively* skewed (Fig. 8-3).

As to the second question, sufficient data are now available to show that with few exceptions, most elements do not follow a Normal distribution in specific types of igneous rocks. Occasionally negative skewness may be observed (for example,

FIG. 8–3   Negatively skewed distribution of SiO_2 in 797 specimens of granite. Note the effect of skewness on the values of the average, median, and mode (average < median < mode).

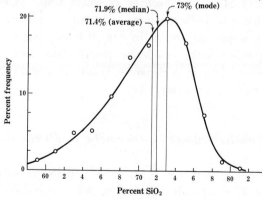

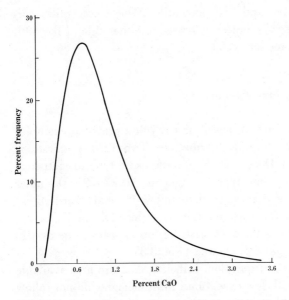

FIG. 8–4 An example of a positively skewed distribution, CaO in 141 specimens of granite; the degree of positive skewness is moderate.

potassium in some granites), but by far the commonest tendency is that of *positive* skewness which is shown by many elements, both common and rare. Two examples of positive skewness are shown in Fig. 8-4, calcium in a suite of 141 granitic rocks (moderate positive skewness); and Fig. 8-5, magnesium in a separate group of granitic rocks (extreme positive skewness).

Positively skewed lognormal-type distributions

Positive skewness is very common in the statistical measurement of element distribution. An examination of several positively skewed distributions shows that they can be normalized

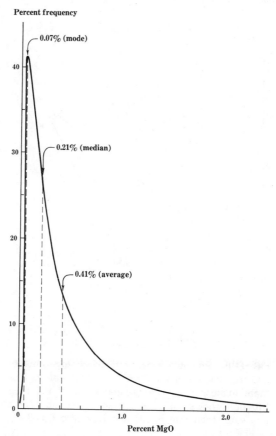

Percent frequency

40

30

20

10

0

0.07% (mode)

0.21% (median)

0.41% (average)

0   1.0   2.0

Percent MgO

FIG. 8–5 An example of extreme positive skewness, magnesium in a suite of granites. Compare the effect of negative skewness (Fig. 8–3) with that of positive skewness on the mode, median, and average (average > median > mode).

or approximately normalized by means of a logarithmic transformation. In other words, if we examine the distribution of the logarithm of the concentration, skewness is either removed or significantly reduced; testing by such means as probability paper shows that the distribution of the logarithm of the concentration is either normal or approximately normal. In these

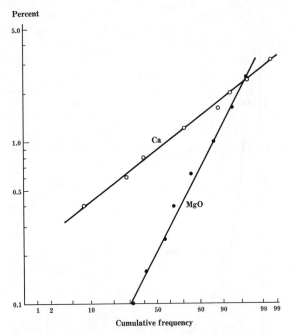

FIG. 8–6 Probability paper tests for lognormality of calcium and magnesium in granites. Both distributions closely approximate lognormality. The greater slope of the magnesium distribution shows that the spread (dispersion) of this element is greater than that of calcium (see also Fig. 8–8).

cases the distribution is said to be lognormal. Examples of tests for lognormality are shown in Fig. 8-6. Whereas in Fig. 8-2 the vertical scale is linear, in Fig. 8-6 it is logarithmic; as before (Fig. 8-2) a close approximation to linearity means that the distribution may be taken to be normal, or actually lognormal in view of the fact that a logarithmic scale is used. It is clear that both calcium and magnesium are lognormally distributed as the drawn straight lines accommodate the plotted points reasonably well. It is clear also, however, that the slopes differ greatly; that of Mg is much greater than that of Ca.

Accordingly, the dispersion of magnesium is much greater than that of calcium. It may be recalled that positive skewness is extreme in the magnesium distribution, much greater than the skewness in the calcium distribution (Fig. 8-4). In general one may say that for distributions of the lognormal type, dispersion increases with increase in positive skewness.

Comparing dispersion (spread) of concentration

It is indeed fortunate that the distribution of many elements follows a single type of statistical distribution which may be quite easily normalized. Estimation and comparison of the dispersion of elements in different rocks is thereby greatly facilitated. For a normally distributed population (SiO_2 in basalt for example), we may present and examine the data in the form of standard deviations of the concentration, or graphically in the form of equal-area frequency distribution diagrams. For the lognormal case, which we are now considering, the procedures are the same except that the logarithm of the concentration is used. In the discussion which follows, a graphical procedure will be used. In order to facilitate comparisons the areas under each curve should be equal and hence the vertical scale is percent frequency. The curves which we are about to consider have been constructed from probability diagrams such as that of Fig. 8-6. Values for constructing the frequency distribution diagrams are read off the fitted line of the cumulative percent frequency diagram at convenient intervals.

Inspection of the equal-area frequency distribution curves of Figs. 8-7 and 8-8 provides a good overall idea of the magnitude and variation of dispersion shown by various elements, abundant and rare, in specific igneous rocks. It is clear that dispersion varies enormously. Compare, for example, the comparatively rare elements, gallium and chromium; the small dispersion of gallium contrasts strongly with the high dispersion of chromium. These two elements may be taken to represent two extremes.

The magnitude of dispersion of a *given* element may vary quite distinctly in different rock types. A clear example is provided by the distribution of vanadium in basalt and in granite (Fig. 8-9). Whereas dispersion of vanadium in basalt is comparatively small, it is extreme in granite. Magnesium is an example of an abundant element which behaves in a similar way: dispersion is small in basalt but extreme in granite (Fig. 8-7).

A satisfactory answer must ultimately be sought to the question, why do elements follow the statistical distribution patterns which they display. In particular, we seek an explanation for the tendency of many elements to follow the positively skewed lognormal type of distribution. Perhaps the reason for

FIG. 8–7 Equal-area frequency distribution diagram for various constituents, mainly the abundant elements, in granitic and basaltic rocks. Compare small dispersion of Ca and Fe in basaltic rocks with Mg (and Co) in granitic rocks.

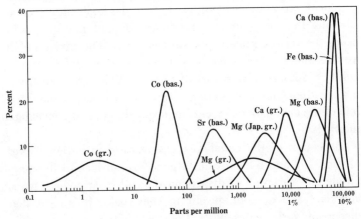

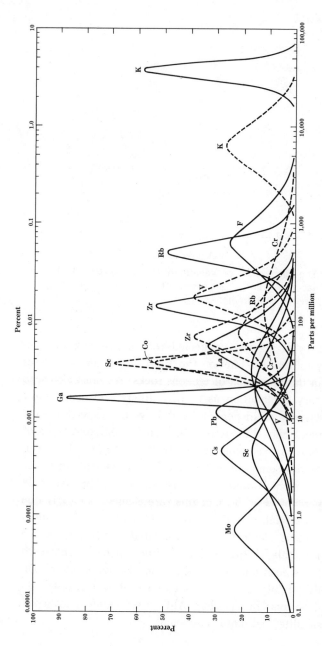

FIG. 8-8 Equal-area frequency distribution diagram for various elements, mainly elements at low concentrations, in a suite of granites (continuous line) and diabases from Canada (dashed line). Note the extremes in dispersion: a minimum for gallium, as compared with an extreme (maximum) dispersion for chromium both in granites and diabases.

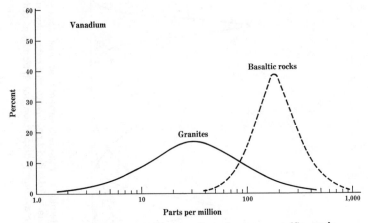

FIG. 8–9 The dispersion of vanadium in two specific rock types, diabase and granite. Dispersion of vanadium in granite is distinctly greater than in diabase.

this tendency is directly connected with the process of fractional crystallization, one of the most important processes involved in the formation of igneous rocks. We must also seek a satisfactory explanation as to why different elements show varying degrees of dispersion, and why the dispersion of a given element may differ quite distinctly in different types of igneous rock. As yet, comparatively little progress has been made. Yet with some elements the principal controlling factor is readily evident. Gallium is a case in point. The strikingly small dispersion (Fig. 8-7) of this rare element is clearly due to its close association with aluminum (Chapter 7). Aluminum is an abundant element and a principal constituent of the common minerals feldspar and mica. Since the early nineteenth century it has been known that the concentration of aluminum varies only slightly in rocks such as basalt and granite; accordingly, because of the close Al-Ga association, the dispersion of "satellite" gallium is also small.

Some final comments

We have touched on several aspects of the distribution of the elements in our planet. Much remains to be done, however, before a clear picture emerges. Good analytical data on the various elements are probably of first importance if the task is to be completed. Heretofore we have suffered greatly from poor analytical data which may lead one along false trails. Though the position now is greatly improved, it is by no means really satisfactory; the analytical chemist must continue to strive toward developing more accurate and sensitive techniques to provide the geochemist with an ever-increasing number of data of the highest quality.

There is a distinct need also to give more thorough consideration to those atomic properties which have controlled the destiny of the elements in our planet. Once our knowledge and understanding of element distributions in the earth improve, however, it may be worthwhile to speculate about other planets. What is their composition? How are the elements distributed and to what extent do "our" geochemical rules of distribution apply? Can we, in fact, predict what might be found on the surfaces and interiors of other planets? We can make predictions which should be sound. Only the future can tell whether or not they are.

APPENDIXES

Appendix A

Estimated abundances of some of the elements in the crust and in chondritic meteorites. Unless otherwise indicated, the values are in parts per million (1 ppm = 0.0001 percent). Arranged in order of atomic number.

Element	Chondrites	Crust	Element	Chondrites	Crust
Li	2.5	20	Ag	0.03–0.1	0.07
Be	0.04	2.8	Cd	0.06	0.2
B	0.43	10	In	0.001	0.1
F	30–130	625	Sn	0.43	2
Na	0.68%	2.4%	Sb	0.10	0.2
Mg	14.4%	1.95%	Te	0.55	
Al	1.3%	8.2%	I	0.04	0.5
Si	17.8%	28.2%	Cs	0.1	3
P	0.11%	1,050	Ba	4.5	425
S	2.3%	260	La	0.34	30
Cl	160	130	Ce	1.1	60
K	0.09%	2.1%	Pr	0.13	8.2
Ca	1.4%	4.2%	Nd	0.61	28
Sc	8.5	22	Sm	0.23	6
Ti	850	0.57%	Eu	0.08	1.2
V	65	135	Gd	0.34	5.4
Cr	3,000	100	Tb	0.052	0.9
Mn	2,600	950	Dy	0.34	3
Fe	25.1%	5.6%	Ho	0.08	1.2
Co	520	25	Er	0.24	2.8
Ni	1.35%	75	Tm	0.034	0.5
Cu	90	55	Yb	0.20	3
Zn	54	70	Lu	0.035	0.5
Ga	5.3	15	Hf	0.19	3
Ge	9.5	1.5	Ta	0.023	2
As	2.2	1.8	W	0.14	1.5
Se	8.5	0.05	Re	0.057	
Br	?	2.5	Os	0.80	
Rb	3	90	Ir	0.60	
Sr	11	375	Pt	1.2	
Y	2	33	Au	0.16	0.004
Zr	12	165	Hg		0.08
Nb	?	20	Tl	0.001	0.45
Mo	1.5	1.5	Pb	0.18	12.5
Ru	1		Bi	0.0025	0.17
Rh	0.17		Th	0.40	9.6
Pd	0.6		U	0.014	2.7

Appendix B

PERIODIC TABLE OF THE ELEMENTS (*Based on Carbon-12 as 12.00000*)

n	I_A	II_A	III_B	IV_B	V_B	VI_B	VII_B	VIII		
1	**1 H** 1.00797	**2 He** 4.0026								
2	**3 Li** 6.939	**4 Be** 9.0122								
3	**11 Na** 22.990	**12 Mg** 24.312								
4	**19 K** 39.102	**20 Ca** 40.08	**21 Sc** 44.956	**22 Ti** 47.90	**23 V** 50.942	**24 Cr** 51.996	**25 Mn** 54.938	**26 Fe** 55.847	**27 Co** 58.933	**28 Ni** 58.71
5	**37 Rb** 85.47	**38 Sr** 87.62	**39 Y** 88.905	**40 Zr** 91.22	**41 Nb** 92.906	**42 Mo** 95.94	**43 Tc** (99)	**44 Ru** 101.07	**45 Rh** 102.91	**46 Pd** 106.4
6	**55 Cs** 132.91	**56 Ba** 137.34	*	**72 Hf** 178.49	**73 Ta** 180.95	**74 W** 183.85	**75 Re** 186.2	**76 Os** 190.2	**77 Ir** 192.2	**78 Pt** 195.09
7	**87 Fr** (223)	**88 Ra** (226)	†							

Transition elements

* *Lanthanide series* (*rare earths*)

† *Actinide series*

57 La 138.91	**58 Ce** 140.12	**59 Pr** 140.91	**60 Nd** 144.24	**61 Pm** (147)	**62 Sm** 150.35	**63 Eu** 151.96
89 Ac (227)	**90 Th** 232.04	**91 Pa** (231)	**92 U** 238.03	**93 Np** (237)	**94 Pu** (244)	**95 Am** (243)

I_B	II_B	III_A	IV_A	V_A	VI_A	VII_A	Inert gases
							2 He 4.0026
		5 B 10.811	6 C 12.011	7 N 14.0067	8 O 15.9994	9 F 18.998	10 Ne 20.183
		13 Al 26.982	14 Si 28.086	15 P 30.974	16 S 32.064	17 Cl 35.453	18 Ar 39.948
29 Cu 63.54	30 Zn 65.37	31 Ga 69.72	32 Ge 72.59	33 As 74.922	34 Se 78.96	35 Br 79.909	36 Kr 83.80
47 Ag 107.870	48 Cd 112.40	49 In 114.82	50 Sn 118.69	51 Sb 121.75	52 Te 127.60	53 I 126.90	54 Xe 131.30
79 Au 196.97	80 Hg 200.59	81 Tl 204.37	82 Pb 207.19	83 Bi 208.98	84 Po (210)	85 At (210)	86 Rn (222)

64 Gd 157.25	65 Tb 158.92	66 Dy 162.50	67 Ho 164.93	68 Er 167.26	69 Tm 168.93	70 Yb 173.04	71 Lu 174.97
96 Cm (247)	97 Bk (247)	98 Cf (251)	99 Es (254)	100 Fm (253)	101 Md (256)	102 No (254)	103 Lw (257)

BIBLIOGRAPHY

1 *How Old is the Earth?* by Patrick M. Hurley, a book in the Science Study Series, Doubleday & Company, Inc., 1959.

Methods in Geochronology by E. Hamilton, Academic Press, Inc., 1965. A text describing the different methods for estimating geological age.

2 *Principles of Geochemistry* by Brian Mason, John Wiley & Sons, Inc., 1958. See Chaps. 2 and 3.

Meteorites by Brian Mason, John Wiley & Sons, Inc., 1962. A general book on meteorite description, classification, composition, and origin.

"A review of atomic abundances in chondrites and the origin of meteorites" by Harold C. Urey, *Reviews of Geophysics*, vol. 2, no. 1, 1964.

The Abundances of the Elements by L. H. Aller, Interscience Publishers, Inc., 1961.

3 *Principles of Geochemistry* by Brian Mason, John Wiley & Sons, Inc., 1958. See Chaps. 2 and 3.

"Crust of the Earth," A. Poldervaart (ed.), *Geological Society of America*, Special Paper 62, 1954.

Several articles, mainly by A. E. Ringwood, which deal with the composition of the earth's mantle have appeared in *Geochimica et Cosmochimica Acta*, Pergamon Press, since 1958.

4 "The significance of the chemical bond for controlling the geochemical distribution of the elements," part 1, by L. H. Ahrens in *Physics and Chemistry of the Earth—V*, Pergamon Press, 1964.

Geochemistry by Kalervo Rankama and Th.G. Sahama, The University of Chicago Press, 1950.

Geochemistry by V. M. Goldschmidt, Clarendon Press, Oxford, 1954. A general text in geochemistry written by one of the founders of geochemistry.

5 *Structural Inorganic Chemistry* by A. F. Wells, Clarendon Press, Oxford, 1962. This book describes the structures of a large number of inorganic substances; solid solution is also discussed (pp. 176–178).

An Introduction to Crystal Chemistry by R. C. Evans, Cambridge University Press, 1964.

6 *Igneous and Metamorphic Petrology* by F. J. Turner and J. Verhoogen, McGraw-Hill Book Company, 1960. This book deals both with igneous rocks and variation diagrams.

Theoretical Petrology by Tom. F. W. Barth, John Wiley & Sons, Inc., 1962. A general text on petrology.

7 "The significance of the chemical bond for controlling the geochemical distribution of the elements," part 1, by L. H. Ahrens, *Physics and Chemistry of the Earth—V*, Pergamon Press, 1964. This article may serve as a reference source to various works on element distributions.

"The application of trace element data to problems of petrology" by S. R. Taylor, *Physics and Chemistry of the Earth—VI*, Pergamon Press, 1965. This article may serve as a reference source to various works on element distributions.

8 "Element distributions in igneous rocks—VII," by L. H. Ahrens. *Geochimica et Cosmochimica Acta 28*, pp. 271–290, 1964. References to various other works on statistical distributions are given in this particular paper.

General comment. There are two journals, *Geochimica et Cosmochimica Acta* (Pergamon Press) and *Geokhimya* (U.S.S.R. Academy of Sciences), which are devoted entirely to geochemistry. A translated version of *Geokhimya* appears regularly, under the title *Geochemistry* (Scripta Technica, Inc.).

INDEX

Catalog

If you are interested in a list of fine Paperback
books, covering a wide range of subjects
and interests, send your name and address,
requesting your free catalog, to:

McGraw-Hill Paperbacks
330 West 42nd Street
New York, New York 10036